Healing the Anxious Woman

Proven Mindful Practices to Relieve
Anxiety, Let Go of Worry, and
Restore Peace and Calm

Maiya Wolf

Table of Contents

DEDICATION 1

INTRODUCTION 3

CHAPTER 1: WHY ME? UNDERSTANDING ANXIETY 5

WHAT IS ANXIETY? 6
STRESS VS. ANXIETY 8
COMMON ANXIETY TRIGGERS 11
MY ANXIETY JOURNEY 12

CHAPTER 2: MIND OVER MATTER 15

WHO AM I? 15
ZENNING OUT 19
MINDFULNESS MAY BE CULTIVATED IN MANY WAYS 19
HOW MINDFULNESS REDUCES ANXIETY 22
STARING INTO THE SHADOW 22
EXERCISES FOR HEALING THE SHADOW SIDE 23
WINDOW TO YOUR SOUL 27

CHAPTER 3: LOVE ME SOME SELF-CARE 31

WHAT DOES SELF-CARE INVOLVE? 31
WHAT IS SELF-LOVE? 33
WHY SELF-LOVE HEALS ANXIETY: A PERSONAL CHOICE 36

CHAPTER 4: EAT, EXERCISE, ENERGIZE, REPEAT 39

STEP 1: EAT 39
WHAT TO EAT 40
WHAT TO AVOID 42
STEP 2: EXERCISE 43
STEP 3: ENERGIZE 48
STEP 4: REPEAT 52

CHAPTER 5: YOU ARE A QUEEN, AND THIS IS YOUR KINGDOM 53

BOUNDARIES 53
TYPES OF BOUNDARIES 55
BARRIERS TO BOUNDARIES 58
BOUNDARIES FOR DIFFERENT SOCIAL SITUATIONS 59
ESTABLISHING YOURS 63
FINAL THOUGHTS 65

CHAPTER 6: THANKING YOUR STARS 67

What Is Gratitude? 67
Gratitude: The Science 68
The Neuroscientific Study of Gratitude 69
Developing Gratitude 72
Gratitude in Nature 73
Gratitude Exercises 75
Spiritual Gratitude 78
Maintaining Gratitude 79
Final Thoughts: Using Gratitude to Combat Anxiety 80

CHAPTER 7: SHOO, NEGATIVITY! 81

What Is Cognitive Behavioral Therapy? 81
Cognitive Behavioral Therapy in Treating Anxiety 82
Cognitive Distortions 83
Cognitive Behavioral Therapy Exercises 96
Final Thoughts on Cognitive Behavioral Therapy 98

CHAPTER 8: FACE YOUR FEARS 99

What Is Exposure Treatment? 99
Types of Exposure Therapy 101
Exposure Therapy: How To Do It at Home 102
A Final Word 104

CHAPTER 9: LEARNING TO LET GO 105

Signs of Radical Acceptance 106
How To Apply Radical Acceptance 108
The Last Word 113

CONCLUSION: A LIFE OF SERENITY 115

ABOUT THE AUTHOR 117

REFERENCES 119

Dedication

I'd like to dedicate this book to my best friend in the whole world, my beautiful mother, and all the incredible women who walk this earth today. Know that you are divine and deserve to be happy, NO MATTER WHAT you have been through or what you may face.

Introduction

Whatever you're doing, anxiety compels you to consider your escape route constantly.

I'll just make up an excuse to get out of it. Or better yet, I'll tell them I have a family emergency!

I would contemplate how to get out of any situation. I had to persuade myself to act like a "normal" human every day, and repeatedly asked myself the following questions:

Why do I have constant anxiety?

What actions can I take to prevent anxiety from controlling my life?

How can I have a life free from worrying over every little thing?

Do you ever find yourself asking any of the questions above? We frequently find ourselves in a cycle of dread, worry, and uncertainty. Anxiety is a real sensation that makes us tense, perplexed, and lonely. It turns our inner workings and our natural world upside down.

I'm writing this book because, as a woman in our current day and age, I believe there is a shortage of resources for those of us who are suffering in our minds, feeling alone, confined, embarrassed, frightened of being misunderstood—or worse, just overlooked.

The lifetime prevalence of anxiety disorders in women is significantly higher than in men (*Anxiety Disorders*, 2019). It is challenging even to discuss the issue, much less take steps to address it.

Men and women experience worry related to their jobs, families, health, and looks. The distinction is that women tend to concentrate their concerns more intensely and frequently on particular topics. We, as women, are more preoccupied with our beauty and the well-being of others than men are for various reasons, including sexism, social pressures, and the lasting effects of conventional gender roles (Chung, 2022).

Additionally, women are more likely to experience stress related to juggling tasks and giving their best effort. We worry about how having one role can interfere with doing another. Perfectionism has frequently been cited as a contributing factor to anxiety symptoms in women, which is related to the problem of juggling responsibilities. We have pressure to succeed and present ourselves gracefully. We worry about our safety because we experience violence more frequently than men, and on top of that, we worry more about our loved ones' safety than our own!

Both genetic predisposition and upbringing can play a role in the development of anxiety. Stress, hormone changes, and genes can all contribute to its development, and due to the considerable hormonal changes that occur throughout puberty, pregnancy, and menopause, women are more likely to experience anxiety at these times (Guarnotta, 2022). And just like men, women are more prone to develop anxiety if they come from anxious families or have been through traumatic or other stressful experiences. I want you to feel understood and connected to other women who are experiencing similar frustrations so we can work together to discover answers and resolve our difficulties.

Before we continue, my name is Maiya Wolf. I've devoted many hours to independent research and study to fully comprehend and further develop my curiosity about the worldwide epidemic of anxiety affecting women.

So many women go through trying situations, and I want them to know they are not alone. As you read on, I hope you will feel a sense of belonging and encouragement to take positive action.

There is never a wrong time to seek help for anxiety. In actuality, holding off too long could result in needless suffering. Anxiety may have far-reaching consequences if left untreated, affecting not only your mood but also your relationships and your capacity to carry out daily tasks at home, school, or work. You may be able to handle your anxiety on your own, if it is minor and does not severely impact your life, if you take care of your mental and physical health and adopt practices that encourage self-love and mindfulness.

Anxiety has the potential to make us feel powerless—this, I know from experience.

Most of the time, you only want to step back undramatically and disappear. Still, as a full-time working mother, wife, business owner, or any combination of these, you *can't* magically disappear. Instead, you may give yourself the blessing of serenity by following one of the numerous methods I outline in this book.

Using these mindful strategies, you are going on a journey to rid yourself of worry, uncover your true purpose in life, and experience inner peace. Proceed with these necessary actions regardless of where you find yourself. You are worth the effort!

Welcome to your healing journey of self-love and finding your inner calm.

Chapter 1:

Why Me? Understanding Anxiety

"Stop worrying so much!"

Although people who suffer from anxiety tend to worry excessively, anxiety and worry are two different things.

On good days, the anxiety isn't so bad that it interferes with your ability to accomplish your job or relax. But on other days, no effort can alleviate the feelings of insecurity, restlessness, and complete devaluation that anxiety brings. While worry can frequently be connected to a stressful event in a person's life, anxiety is not always rational.

"Why don't you just relax?"

Most people urge their anxious loved ones to calm down because they honestly believe that would make them feel better, but that is rarely the case. If we could easily "relax" whenever we wanted to, we would have done so!

"Have you ever tried XYZ?"

Dealing with the notion that everyone will attempt to manage your anxiety problem for you, whether or not you want them to, is a necessary component of treating an anxiety disorder. How frequently have you been questioned about your coffee intake and asked if you exercise daily? Multiple times, I'm sure.

People frequently recommend coping mechanisms that you have previously tried out or adopted. Therefore, their "advice" is seldom helpful. Probing us repeatedly about our routines might feel more like an interrogation than a friendly discussion about our mental health.

As an anxious individual, you've most probably tried all helpful suggestions regarding anxiety management. So, hearing the same simple advice over and over serves us no purpose. These phrases we hear almost daily ultimately lead us down a further path of anxiety and self-doubt. Well, you may ask, why isn't any advice working for me? Am I just hopeless?

No. You are most certainly not!

To conquer your battles, you must first understand what they are. So, let's have a look at what exactly anxiety is and how we can move forward.

What Is Anxiety?

Anxiety can be characterized by feelings of worry, fear, and unease. It is a normal reaction to stressful situations, such as solving a challenging situation at work, taking an examination, or making an important decision. It can aid in coping. You could feel more energized or able to concentrate when you're experiencing it. However, the fear might be overpowering and persistent for those who suffer from anxiety disorders.

Am I Anxious?

Anxiety is natural and essential when confronted with potentially dangerous or frightening situations.

Since the beginning of time, humans have had physical alarms that enable them to take evasive action from predators or when danger is nearby. These warnings manifest as a rapid heart rate, excessive sweating, and a heightened awareness of your environment.

This "fight-or-flight" response, brought on by the adrenaline surge caused by said threat, is a hormonal and chemical messenger that the brain produces. This makes people physically capable of fending off or escaping potential dangers.

For modern humans, the need to flee from predators and other threats is less of an immediate issue than it used to be. Work, money, family, health, and other important matters that require a person's attention but don't always call for the fight-or-flight reaction are the primary sources of anxiety today.

How Did This Come to Be?

Knowing what might trigger or worsen your anxiety can be quite helpful in controlling it. Still, since everyone experiences anxiety differently, it can be challenging to pinpoint the precise source of the anxiety. Numerous elements are likely at play.

The Risk Factors

You may be more likely to develop an anxiety disorder if you experience one or more of the following:

- **Trauma:** Children who experienced maltreatment, suffered trauma, or saw distressing events are more likely to get anxiety disorders later in life. Anxiety disorders can also manifest in adults who had traumatizing experiences.
- **Stress brought on by illness:** A serious health condition or disease might result in anxiety.
- **Stress accumulation:** Excessive anxiety may be brought on by a significant incident or a build-up of minor stressful life circumstances, such as a loss in the family, stress at work, or financial worries.
- **Personality:** Some personality types are more predisposed to anxiety problems than others (as you will learn later).
- **Other mental health issues:** Anxiety disorders are frequently present in people who also suffer from other mental health issues like depression, ADHD, OCD, and so on.
- **Family matters**: Anxiety disorders have been shown to run in families. Thus, having a close blood member with the disease may increase your risk.
- **Alcohol or drugs:** Alcohol, drug abuse, or withdrawal from these can increase or induce anxiety.

Steps You Can Take

You may take steps to control your anxiety once you are more aware of its sources. As you read on, you will discover what the root of your anxiety stems from.

Determine Your Triggers

Knowing what could trigger your anxiety or make it worse can be useful in managing it. However, identifying that trigger or impulse might be challenging if you have more than one.

Plan and Control Your Trigger

Before any chaos occurs, be sure to attend to your basic human needs. You need to take care of yourself, too. It's crucial to consider how you may prepare for the inevitable challenges by caring for yourself now.

As soon as feelings of anxiety surface, it is time to employ one of the many coping strategies within this book.

Sharing your feelings with others might help you feel more validated and overcome the worry that the trigger has brought on. The sooner these triggers are recognized and addressed, the better for anxiety management. The strategies and tools are here to help you find a happy medium. Find what works best for you and stick to it.

Anxiousness can range from mild to severe, but anybody who often experiences the latter should seek professional help. A doctor can assist if you believe your anxiety has gotten out of hand and is at a critical stage. Remedies do exist.

Stress vs. Anxiety

When it comes to the difference between stress and anxiety, the line is thin. Both are feelings, but stress usually results from something happening in the outside world. A job deadline or an argument with a loved one, for example, are short-term triggers. Long-term triggers include chronic disease, prejudice, or being unable to work.

The Difference Between Stress and Anxiety

Despite some similar mental and physical symptoms, these two conditions have completely distinct causes. Identifying which one you have is essential to creating a successful treatment strategy and feeling better.

It may be challenging to distinguish between stress and anxiety, however, as both have similar biological reactions and symptoms.

External Factors Are Common in Stress

Stress often lasts a brief time and is a reaction to a perceived threat.

In most cases, stress is a reaction to an external reason, such as a pressing deadline for a new work project or a disagreement with your partner. This usually goes away after the issue has been handled. Since external variables contribute to stress, addressing them head-on might be beneficial. There are various strategies to manage and lessen your symptoms if you are under continuous, chronic stress, such as engaging in physical activity, using deep breathing techniques, getting enough sleep, and setting aside time to interact with others.

Anxiety Is an Exaggerated Response to a Particular Situation

Anxiety can persist and occasionally feel like nothing is setting it off. An individual's response to stress is unique and has an internal source. A persistent sensation of dread or concern in circumstances that are not genuinely dangerous is a common feature of anxiety.

Anxiety can develop in response to encountering a new person, location, or circumstance, and it may represent an extreme overreaction that causes you to react inappropriately and severely.

Anxiety Can Impair Performance

When anxiety strikes, people search for the proper reaction and response. But occasionally, they are paralyzed by uncertainty and powerless to take action. This inability to perform makes a person feel immobile and trapped when faced with difficulty.

Anxiety Produces Irrational Fear

Compared to stress, anxiety frequently manifests as fear or dread that, at low levels, might feel like nervousness or worry and, at high ones, feels like panic. At lesser levels, stress might make some individuals feel pressured or overwhelmed.

Specific Symptoms Indicate an Anxiety Disorder

An underlying illness is frequently indicated by persistent anxiety. It's common for people with anxiety disorders to see a correlation between increased stress and worsening symptoms. Still, it's also possible for them to suffer symptoms even when they're not under stress.

Symptoms

The majority of the symptoms of stress and anxiety are the same, including:

- higher heart rate
- difficulty sleeping
- muscular tension
- anger
- irritability
- dizziness
- brain fog
- headaches

- increased sweating
- feeling overwhelmed
- restlessness
- change in appetite
- a sense of impending disaster
- feeling tingly or numb
- stomach problems, such as diarrhea and nausea

Can One Change Into the Other?

Although stress can cause anxiety or exacerbate pre-existing anxiety, not everyone experiences these effects. Some people may not feel anxiety symptoms even when stress levels are high. Anxiety might be viewed as a more persistent stress reaction that is frequently aroused yet tricky to extinguish. More sophisticated responses may occur when the fight-or-flight mechanism is triggered for prolonged periods.

How to Recognize Stress or Anxiety in Yourself

Consider your current circumstances by taking a step back. What types of things bother you the most? Are there particular risks or occurrences?

Stress is to blame if you can link a particular event or circumstance to your feelings. However, if the precise cause is unclear or your symptoms continue after the initial stimulus disappears, anxiety could be the reason.

Common Anxiety Triggers

Socializing

- **Social gatherings or parties:** You're not alone if the idea of being in a room with strangers doesn't sound like fun. Social anxiety disorder is a term used to describe the anxiety that might be brought on by situations when you have to engage in small talk or socialize with strangers.
- **Public performances or gatherings:** Anxiety is frequently brought on by public speaking, speaking in front of others, competing, or even simply reading aloud.

Traumatic Events

Childhood, adolescence, or adulthood traumatic events frequently launch anxiety disorders. A particularly significant influence is likely to be had when stress and trauma occur while a person is very young. Experiences like the following can lead to anxiety issues:

- verbal or physical abuse
- the loss of a loved one
- racism, social alienation, or bullying
- neglect from parents or guardians
- overprotective parents

How You Find Yourself in the Present Moment

Your current troubles in life may also make you anxious. For instance:

- any conflict with a partner, family member, friend, or co-worker
- a lot of change or uncertainty, causing a build-up of stress
- weariness from not getting proper rest or nutrition
- drinking too much caffeine or other stimulating supplements
- strain from lengthy or demanding work hours, deadlines or expectations to meet
- financial issues or not having a job
- experiencing medical issues, either physical or mental
- thinking negatively about yourself and others
- clinging to perfectionism in all your daily tasks
- issues with housing security or homelessness
- worries about natural disasters or the environment
- pregnancy concerns or the well-being of your child(ren)

Information Overload

Additionally, the amount of social media you use might cause anxiety. All of the following are linked to an elevated risk of anxiety:

- using at least four different social media platforms
- spending at least one hour every day on social media
- visiting social networking sites at least 30 times a week
- having a strong emotional attachment to social media
- a sense of addiction to social media

My Anxiety Journey

I was diagnosed with Secondary Depression and Generalized Anxiety Disorder (GAD) when I was 15 years old. At the time, I was terrified by the diagnosis. I was sure to be the only girl in school who needed therapy. I didn't know anyone else who was so anxious they had to take a little pink pill or sometimes breathe into a brown paper bag to calm themselves down.

Sometimes anxiety has no apparent cause. I'd do everything to avoid entering a place where I didn't know anyone and didn't have a task at hand to keep me busy. I got nervous driving because I feared that someone would hit me. I was scared to be around others because I thought they might be able to see through my cracks and realize that I was just strange and unlikeable. Whenever I was home alone for over an hour, I'd get nervous because my mind would start spiraling into thoughts about my loved ones getting into danger—if they didn't pick up their phone right away, I was certain that something terrible had happened to them. Everything worried me! I was always on edge.

Eventually I married a man who I, naively, believed would become some sort of hero in my anxiety battles, only to discover another level of struggle. Our marriage was riddled with challenges. My husband turned out to be a pornography addict. Since the foundation of our intimate life was built around this issue, it gave way for many other conflicts to arise. My already low self-confidence came crashing down, and I began to experience extreme self-esteem issues around my body. I could never measure up to the unreal women on the internet, and I believed I was ugly, undesirable, and ultimately, worthless. Immobilizing emotions of helplessness and depression would start to kick in, and when paired with my anxiety, I became like a ticking time bomb, a mix of insanity and sorrow. I was triggered every time friends or family would ask me how my husband and I were doing, when we were planning on having kids, or worse, how our sex life was. Terrified of being judged and misunderstood, I would swiftly try to detour the conversation before shutting down completely. I lived with this darkness in my head and in my heart, and every day I wondered when the pain would end—and if I would ever feel happy, loved, peace, and calm again.

Despite the struggles, we did eventually have two beautiful children, but the mountain of stress and uncertainty only grew with becoming a parent. At first, like any mom, I worried about their survival. "Have they eaten enough?" "Are they supposed to be that color?" "Are they still breathing?!" As my children got older, my thoughts evolved to a more self-sabotaging style. I felt like I was never good enough for them. If I didn't have a meal ready on time, or if I was busy finishing chores, I believed I was neglecting them and beat myself up. Slowly, I even convinced myself that I was unfit to raise them. I questioned my purpose in life and often blamed God for my circumstances. I wondered if I'd ever be the parent and person I truly wanted to be—joyful, grounded, and FREE OF SUFFERING.

It wasn't until one morning, when I was feeling overwhelmed with loneliness and completely burnt out from my self-imposed expectations regarding my children, that I knew it had all gone too far. I put on a movie for my kids and locked myself away in my room. My whole body melted to the floor and I proceeded to have the worst panic attack of my life. I truly thought I might die and *that* was absolutely terrifying. I had reached my breaking point and knew that I couldn't exist any longer living the way that I was. I needed to find coping methods to overcome the relentless monster in my head that was robbing me of my joy and freedom. There was no other option. My desire to heal became urgent.

I dove into extensive self-study, reading countless books by respected authors, listening to educational podcasts, and devouring every bit of wisdom I could on how to improve my mental state and very being. I needed to spend time determining what worked and what didn't. There were days when I was hopeful and things started to feel more positive, and other days when everything would fall apart all over again. Still, I kept working at it no matter what.

Coupled with occasional counseling and some medication, I started to feel a little better as I explored a new world of mindful healing for anxiety. I became passionate about the subject of mental health and finding ways to be more intentional in maintaining a strong and healthy mind. Eventually, my confidence grew and I started to share my knowledge with people around me.

I spent countless hours working with educated mentors and researchers who had studied mindful practice in-depth and other alternative coping strategies for anxiety. I knew this science-backed research would be a turning point for many women who needed sound evidence before attempting various methods.

I understand how frustrating it is to feel helpless in the face of a problem that appears to devour you every waking moment. No matter how hard you try, you feel like you can't keep up with the world. But after years of struggles and suffering, I have found that long-term healing has been made possible by assisting myself and other women in incorporating easy-to-do mindful practices into our daily lives.

Now, I have the chance to share this with you in the hopes that you will start on your own journey to heal and find peace.

Chapter 2:

Mind Over Matter

Now that we've discussed anxiety, let's dive into how to implement certain tools to help ease your anxious mind!

Mindfulness practice naturally allows the mind to find itself: this is accurate self-awareness. Mindfulness meditation teaches you that not every feeling or thought warrants a reaction. It assists you in prioritizing and making better use of your energy and time.

Who Am I?

What Is Self-Awareness?

"Awareness" is a popular expression within introspection and mindfulness discussions. But what exactly is it? Is it mental alertness? Discerning? Being well-educated? Is there a distinction between consciousness and awareness? Are self-consciousness and self-awareness the same thing?

Knowing, realizing, or perceiving something is how most dictionaries characterize awareness. We may become conscious of a predicament, a remedy, a philosophy, a presence, a sensation, a concept, or an emotion. Focusing on the present moment is what awareness means when discussing mindfulness practice.

Self-Awareness Areas

Here is a list of some self-awareness areas you need to keep in mind as you go forward:

Personality

Normally, our personalities, values, and wants don't alter from what we discover about ourselves. Knowing ourselves and the environments in which we thrive and those in which we don't is essential for achieving success and minimizing stress.

Values

We should all be aware of and committed to our ideals. It's quite simple to lose track of your highest priorities daily, moment by moment. The difficulties and opportunities throughout the workday cause us to quickly accumulate more "things to do" than we have time for. It's easy to waste time on less essential tasks since so few truly matter to us, so we need to establish our values and know what we stand for. We will be less likely to deter from what really matters to us.

Habits

We all likely have at least one habit that hinders our effectiveness, even though we would like to only have the "good" habits that allow us to manage and connect with people efficiently. Habits and routines form our very being! It's so important to keep a watchful eye on them.

Needs

Various psychological wants, such as esteem, love, belongingness, accomplishment, self-actualization, power, and control, are the main motivators of our activities and encounters. Understanding how our needs affect our interpersonal interactions is one of the benefits of recognizing which needs have the most significant impact on our behavior. Needs motivate us, and when they aren't met, they may lead to tension, conflict, and anger.

Emotions

One of the five elements of emotional intelligence, emotional self-awareness, has recently gained much attention. Emotional self-awareness is the knowledge of your feelings, their origins, and how they affect your decisions and behavior. Someone with a high emotional self-awareness is more aware of the underlying function behind their emotions and can thus effectively regulate them.

What Is the Significance of Self-Awareness?

Today's fast-paced lifestyles bring elevated stress, anxiety, and a propensity for repressed feelings to bubble to the surface. Many people experience pressure in the chest or the pit of their abdomen. Some complain about being sad and unsatisfied for no apparent cause. Instead of recognizing and dealing with our feelings, we frequently "look the other way" and try to dismiss them through various diversions.

The only remedy with a long-term effect is self-awareness. When individuals gain self-awareness, they can better recall their ideas, feelings, and bodily sensations. They can perceive themselves from a new, more honest perspective. It may also reveal deep-rooted feelings that they were previously unaware of.

How Do We Apply Self-Awareness?

Here are suggestions for increasing self-awareness through practical methods:

Recognize and Accept Your Feelings

Society encourages us to make rational judgments and leave our emotions out of the equation. In reality, our emotions frequently speak for us! We can be thrown off balance if we don't include them in our thinking process. We need to find the balance of combining our emotions with rational cognition when making critical judgments. It's important to investigate your feelings and trust your instincts. Don't give anything the go-ahead if your feelings and practical reasoning are at odds.

Go Beyond Your Sensations

Self-awareness is more than simply being aware of your feelings and emotions; it's also about applying what you learn to present-day living. With self-awareness, you can tell which events and emotions deplete or make you uneasy and which fill you with purpose and joy. We need to seek the things that make us feel more alive.

Adopt a Growth Mentality

Becoming used to your daily routine or doing things a certain way is normal. When we have been doing something for a while, we tend to believe our way is the only correct one. However, if we adopt a growth or development mindset, we recognize that even our most fundamental skills can be improved through practice and experience.

Define Limits

We sometimes have trouble focusing and taking an honest inventory of ourselves when we don't know our limits, or if we don't define them well enough. Working long hours, spending time with negative people, and binge-watching another episode on Netflix all make it difficult to pause, think, and become self-aware. Setting limits ties hand-in-hand with having boundaries, which we will look at later.

Identify Harmful Behaviors

Certain behaviors are blatantly destructive for us. Some examples are staying up late every night to scroll mindlessly on your phone instead of getting some sleep, drinking alcohol, or using other numbing substances instead of being present and prioritizing your health needs.

Recognize Your Blind Spots

Being aware of your blind spots and attempting to eliminate them are crucial components of self-awareness. Blind spots include refusing assistance, a conviction that you are always correct, or a desire to avoid difficult talks. If you recognize these tendencies in yourself, you can attempt to change them or, at the very least, be honest about them when things become challenging or conflict arises.

Assist Others in Developing Self-Awareness

If we can master the habit of being self-aware in our own lives, we can extend that tool to our loved ones. Imagine how that can change our experiences and surroundings into healing, acceptance, and growth!

Zenning Out

Being mindful is being aware of your thoughts, feelings, and sensations in each moment. Mindfulness is intended to let our ideas, feelings, and senses come and go without interference or desire to react to them.

It entails a soft acceptance of everything that briefly enters your awareness. Instead of focusing so much on accomplishing a particular goal, you should explore your experience and increase your understanding of the factors that excite you, drive you, and encourage your progress, as well as the ones that prevent you from moving forward. You will learn more about how your views, emotions, and sensations affect each other, your mood, and how you interact with the outside world as you practice mindfulness.

Meditation is built around understanding yourself. Mindfulness meditation may help you control your stress and anxiety levels and can even help you relax if you have panic attacks. You may quiet your body and mind by using this meditation practice to help slow down your racing thoughts, lessen negativity, and alleviate your mind (Star, 2021).

Mindfulness May Be Cultivated in Many Ways

Being mindful might be challenging at first, but it becomes easier as you learn to focus your thoughts and intentions.

Methods for Implementing Mindfulness

There are several ways to facilitate the practice of mindfulness. Below are just some of my favorites:

Pay Attention to One Thing at a Time

If you use it properly, your to-do list can become an act of mindfulness. Give one task your complete and undivided attention for ten minutes. No multitasking, including phone scrolling, clicking notifications, or browsing the internet, is allowed! Let that one task be the main focus until the timer runs out.

Observe Your Body's Feelings and Sensations

Gently move your focus around your body to take note of any feelings. Your feelings are only the surface of a universe of wisdom. Perhaps you feel "dead" or "heavy" inside. Don't feel compelled to analyze, understand, or change those feelings. Instead, try to let them be. Take note of them. And after allowing them to be, release them with a deep breath of acceptance.

Explore the Urges You Have

Allow any desires or cravings that come to your attention to exist and pay attention to how these make you feel without doing anything else. We tend to want to respond right away when an impulse strikes us, yet when we act out on our urges instinctively, without thinking, some of our habits or addictions actually cause us more harm than good. Instead of taking action to immediately satisfy a temptation, attempt to sit with it as long as you are able to. Approach it with curiosity, and know that it will go away in its own time.

Practice Guided Meditation

Finding a small, quiet area and using a mindfulness app is all it takes to practice meditation. Apps and online courses are excellent ways to try it out without devoting a lot of time or enrolling in a costly class.

Eat Mindfully

As with talking, thinking, reading, browsing emails, and watching TV, eating is one of those actions we do almost without thinking. If you want to eat mindfully, focus solely on the sensation of eating without any outside interruptions. The most effective approach to care for ourselves is through food. As you eat, take note of any ideas or emotions that arise. Are you nourishing yourself? What emotions do you have after eating? Happiness? Warmth? Guilt? Resist the need to criticize your ideas or feelings. There are no correct or incorrect responses, only learning.

Clouds of Thought

To practice mindfulness, you must take a "step back" from your ideas and observe them rather than allowing them to become ingrained or give rise to unfavorable emotions. One technique is to visualize your thoughts as clouds in the sky.

Imagine seeing your thoughts like you might observe clouds: without analysis or judgment and with a sense of detachment. The issue with our thoughts is that they tend to linger and develop into feelings. Give them room to move instead so they can gently drift away. After letting them in, let them out. If you find that certain thoughts become fixed or persistent, try focusing on your breathing and being present.

Make an Effort to Do What You Love

You should give your full attention to whatever you're doing now, whether dining, reading, strolling, having a warm bath, or being with a loved one. Be present at that moment and commit to whatever you are doing. We all have that one thing that we get lost in when we become so immersed in our tasks that we lose track of time. For me, it's writing and painting. I love experiencing my emotions on a canvas or piece of paper. If you're finding it hard to fully immerse yourself at the moment, shift your thoughts and actions to something you love—and lose yourself for a moment doing just that.

How Mindfulness Reduces Anxiety

With mindfulness, you may learn to stay with challenging emotions without analyzing, stifling, or encouraging them. Your anxieties, irritations, unpleasant memories, and other challenging thoughts and emotions frequently disappear when you allow yourself to feel and recognize them.

By practicing mindfulness, you can safely examine the root causes of your tension and concerns. Going with what's occurring rather than fighting it or running away from it gives you a chance to understand what's motivating your worries.

Staring Into the Shadow

It's always just out of sight, directly behind us, our shadow.

Within the mindfulness approach, the term "shadow" refers to everything about ourselves that we are unable to see. It is much simpler to see someone else's shadow before realizing our own.

By delving into your dark side, you can find your true self and experience a surge of inspiration, vitality, and self-awareness. Introspection is crucial for developing into a well-balanced, mature individual!

Each of us has qualities that we are proud of and qualities in which we lack confidence. We conceal some of these characteristics from the public eye because they may irritate or humiliate us. Your shadow self is made up of these components and wants to be heard.

Accepting and facing your shadow can be a challenging process. It is human nature to resist that which is hard and uncomfortable, especially when it comes to difficult or ugly things within ourselves. So, we instinctively repress it.

Our shadow is still there but dismissed to the background and forgotten.

However, suppressing your inner shadow might have harmful negative effects. The shadow typically appears as our triggers, which are emotional responses that we haven't fully processed and that surface when certain conditions are present. Constructively facing your dark side requires practice, introspection, direction, and courage!

Shadow work is a process that aims to help you accept and embrace every part of your identity so that you can go through life with greater ease and authenticity. Know, love, and accept yourself wholeheartedly.

What Does Shadow Work Aim to Achieve?

Your shadow is a normal aspect of who you are, not a problem or an error.

The main goal of shadow work is to increase self-awareness, which leads to self-acceptance and compassion. Delving into your shadow means that you may face difficult feelings from past traumas that have been concealed, repressed, or shamed. If your shadow is connected to trauma, then your "work" would be to embrace every aspect of yourself that might have been repressed for years. And this is much easier said than done.

Knowing your shadow gives you the power to take charge of your life and encourages you to lead a more purposeful and conscious existence. As you become more accepting of your true self, you will become more confident in your journey and what you had to go through to get where you are today.

Exercises for Healing the Shadow Side

Your true self yearns to be discovered and understood. It seeks recognition and an opportunity to manifest. Here are some suggestions for how to use shadow work for healing:

Pay Close Attention to How You Feel

Observing your thoughts, feelings, and behaviors, as well as the situations that set them off, is one of the best ways to learn to know your inner self.

Knowing how your habits affect your daily life is much clearer once you make an effort to acknowledge them. Keep an open mind and avoid self-criticism or shame as you notice your instinctive behaviors.

Once you understand them, you'll be able to recognize your inner shadow more efficiently and consider its motivations. To understand the source of your sentiments, pay attention to the circumstances that led to your reaction.

Put It in Writing

Journaling is one of the most practical shadow work examples. It's a safe and easy approach to communicating positive and negative thoughts in your own space and time.

While your journal is an attempt to understand your shadow, think about the following:

- childhood traumas, including any instances of abuse or neglect
- what you think other people think of you and how it makes you feel
- memories that make you feel bad
- the worst qualities you observe in others and instances in which you have shown those qualities
- things that make you nervous or uncomfortable

Whatever method you use, commit to it regularly, be truthful, and don't self-censor. This profound type of journaling will probably make you feel uneasy initially, but you will gradually become more comfortable as you write.

How Can Journaling Reduce Anxiety?

Journaling is a fantastic coping mechanism.

Writing in an anxiety diary offers quick and momentary relief from overpowering thoughts. It enables you to acknowledge and even welcome nervous thoughts. Writing things down forces you to confront your weaknesses, which might help you feel less stressed in the long run.

There is research to support it! We now know that keeping a positive affect journal (PAJ) can help alleviate stress and sadness and boost your overall happiness (Wooll, 2022). People can better understand themselves and identify areas for improvement by writing down their thoughts and feelings. The practice of putting ideas and feelings into words helps you recognize them.

It's crucial to have a safe place to express yourself. It's important to note everything stressing you out in your journal without fearing it could bother your loved ones. Writing in a diary is a beneficial method to express yourself in privacy.

When everything around you seems to be in utter chaos, putting pen to paper might help you establish order. By sharing your most personal worries, thoughts, and feelings you come to know yourself. Consider the time you spend writing as personal downtime. This is your time to unwind...

Journaling Exercises for Anxiety

These writing topics are intended as a starting point to begin journaling for anxiety relief. You can then decide whether to keep using prompts or attempt free writing. There is no incorrect way to capture your thoughts and feelings!

Try the following prompts:

- Did I experience any anxiety or tension today? If so, what set off that emotion, and how did I deal with it?
- Which one of my morning habits would I wish to change?
- What change would I like to make to my nightly routine?
- If I did _____, what would happen? List the advantages and disadvantages.
- What do I fear the most? Why?
- Where in my body do I experience anxiety?
- What caused me to feel afraid or nervous today?
- To what extent can I reduce my anxiety symptoms, and what strategies can I use?
- How would life be different if I could manage my anxiety instead of constantly feeling like it has power over me?
- Consider what caused the fear with curiosity and without passing judgment.

There is no single journey to mastering journaling as an anxiety treatment. The most important thing is to give it a try.

Show Off Your Artistic Side

In its many forms, art is an excellent means of self-expression and self-discovery. Art can assist you in developing personal awareness and understanding of yourself, and can promote healing—especially in your mental health.

If journaling isn't your thing, think about finding other creative outlets. Try things like singing, dancing, sculpting, painting, and drawing. Let your inner self express itself in whatever form it wants to without judging or censoring it. Put on your favorite tunes and dance your heart out, or grab a canvas and paint what you feel. Explore and find what works best for you!

Ask for Assistance

While it is certainly possible to complete shadow work independently, you could also consider engaging a qualified professional's assistance.

If you have dealt with losses, abuses, neglect, or inherited problems from previous generations, therapy can help tremendously. Therapists can assist you in exploring your shadow self to become more aware of the feelings you frequently brush aside or deny.

Apply the Mirror Method

Applying the Mirror Method usually means that you can acknowledge your shadow self and see that it exhibits the same qualities and behaviors that you dislike in others. You don't fully accept these aspects as part of your identity, so you must first acknowledge these traits in others before you can work on them yourself.

Consider a person you dislike or with whom you struggle. What is it specifically that bothers you about them? These traits or characteristics are likely the ones you've buried deep inside yourself that should be dug out and brought to the surface—and examined more deeply. In contrast, the traits you admire in others tend to show qualities you aspire to be.

Talk to the Shadow Version of Yourself

If you give your shadow self strength by ignoring it, then power is taken away when you address it. When intense emotions surface, talk to them instead of dismissing them.

As you wait for your shadow's response, ask questions. Maintain your objectivity and be receptive to its answers. Ask "why?" repeatedly to reveal your shadow self's many layers. *Why did XYZ act as a trigger? Why did I experience XYZ? What bothers me about XYZ?*

Make Use of Affirmations

You can rewire your brain and way of thinking by using affirmations. Effectively and consciously change your mentality, increase your self-assurance, and boost your self-esteem. Affirmations can also calm and reassure you when you're experiencing stress.

To help you get started, consider these:

- *My past does not define me.*
- *I have grown as a person by overcoming my emotions.*
- *I have decided to accept my past as it is.*
- *I embrace and adore who I truly am.*
- *I accept responsibility for my errors.*
- *I pardon those who have mistreated me.*

Shadow work tasks are challenging. It can be tough to confront your demons and the hidden aspects of yourself. It requires bravery and perseverance, but trust me, it is worthwhile. Remember to treat yourself with kindness and compassion, and to be patient with the process.

Window to Your Soul

When people are together, self-awareness and personal growth can be improved. An easy way to accomplish this goal of comprehending and enhancing communication between group members is to employ the Johari Window Model. This paradigm was created in 1955 by American psychologists Harry Ingham and Joseph Luft (*The Johari Window Model*, 2014). Joseph Luft developed the concept after researching group dynamics at the University of California. By combining their two first names, the pair came up with the name "Johari."

What Is the Johari Window?

The Johari Window is a model designed to help people understand how others see them. This concept is based on the notion that trust may be built by disclosing personal information to others and listening to their feedback. The four window panes or quadrants of the Johari model each represent one individual. Each of the four window panes represents a personal trait.

The Johari Window

Arena (known to others and known to self)	**Blind Spot** (known to others, but not known to self)
Facade (known to self, but not known to others)	**Unknown** (Not known to self and also not known to others)

Modeling the Johari Window

A four-paned standard window is how a Johari is pictured, and this model interprets how feedback is delivered and received. Two panes reveal how you view yourself and attempt to present yourself to the world. The other two panes reflect the portion of the self that is hidden from yourself but visible to others. This social interaction activity allows information to flow from one window to the next, and mutual trust can be developed through group members' input.

The Johari Window is a straightforward procedure during which people may see their advantages, disadvantages, and blind spots. This can be a great exercise to try with friends or family, or even trusted colleagues, as it allows you to see the side of yourself that others experience. Choose your participants wisely! They should be people who spend a lot of time with you and know you well on some level, whether personally or professionally.

The exercise works as follows:

1. Participants choose the predetermined number of descriptors they believe best describe them. You can refer to the upcoming list of descriptors.

2. Next, the participant chooses the adjectives that best characterize a different individual using the same list of words.

3. The adjectives are then chosen and put into one of four windows:
   - **Arena:** Qualities you choose for yourself, as well as qualities chosen by others for you. These are usually the dominant or most noticeable features of a person. "Everyone recognizes me as X."
   - **Blind Spot:** Characteristics that you did not choose for yourself but that others chose for you. They could be unidentified subconscious traits or impressions. "I didn't realize that I was perceived as X."
   - **Facade:** Characteristics you choose for yourself but that others did not. Defining features not immediately apparent to the naked eye. "I don't share that, yet I feel like there is X in me. You don't see it?"
   - **Unknown:** Neither you nor anybody else chose these traits. Irrelevant features that are either unknown or irrelevant. "I am not X."

4. Allow each participant to check their Johari Window evaluation once everyone has finished. It is encouraged that everyone contrasts their evaluations with each other.

5. To get a person to open up, you may have them discuss an adjective the person picked out for themselves, but the group didn't.

6. Ask the person to choose one of the words the group has chosen but they have yet to choose. Now the group can comment on why they chose this descriptor for the person.

Descriptor List to Describe a Person

This is merely to serve as an example. Feel free to add your own characteristics and descriptions.

- adventurous
- ambitious
- artistic
- assertive
- balanced
- compassionate
- competitive
- charismatic
- courageous
- determined
- direct
- dynamic
- easygoing
- emotional
- enthusiastic
- forgiving
- helpful
- honest
- independent
- knowledgeable
- kind
- logical
- loving
- mature
- motivated
- open-minded
- passionate
- perceptive
- persistent
- practical
- responsible
- sensitive
- sociable
- thoughtful
- understanding

Take Advantage of Your Experience

Having an open attitude toward the activity can help you gain the most. Since you don't know what you don't know, you can often find the most valuable wisdom that elevates your life when you least expect it. Additionally, I recommend that you have several people complete your Johari Window. Doing so allows you to see any outliers and character traits that appear more than once.

Chapter 3:

Love Me Some Self-Care

First things first: self-care is not the same as self-indulgence or selfishness, which is a common misconception. Practicing self-care means prioritizing your own needs so you can meet the needs of others better and get everything done that you set out to do each day.

Social, emotional, and psychological health are all parts of mental health. Everything, from our internal processes to our external interactions and decisions, is influenced. When it comes to your physical and emotional well-being, nothing is more important than your mental health! If you suffer from a mental health condition, taking care of yourself can help you stay healthy and strengthen your commitment to getting better.

What Does Self-Care Involve?

Self-care is making time for activities that enhance your quality of life and physical and mental health. It has several benefits for your overall well-being, including stress management, a decreased chance of sickness, and a boost in energy. The exercises and practices you regularly perform, no matter how minor they may seem, can have a significant positive influence. Each individual's definition of self-care is different, so it's vital to discover what works best for you, which may require some trial and error. Self-care isn't a cure-all for mental illness. Still, it may help you manage your condition by identifying and addressing the things that worsen your symptoms and the ones that help you feel better.

Different Forms of Self-Care

Anything that makes you happy is fair game, and this includes anything that leaves you feeling taken care of.

Self-care can be divided into a few distinct types:

- **Emotional:** Practices include self-talk, regular bubble baths, saying "no" to unnecessary demands, permitting yourself to take a moment and just pause, and scheduling weekly coffee dates with friends.
- **Physical:** This includes setting aside enough time for sleep, establishing a regular exercise schedule, and selecting wholesome foods over heavily processed meals.
- **Spiritual:** Practices include meditating, going outside and spending time in nature, performing random acts of kindness, maintaining a gratitude diary, and participating in religious activities.

Starting a Self-Care Practice

Find the things that make you happy, give you energy, and help you feel balanced. Start small by deciding on one action you want to integrate into your routine throughout the upcoming week, then build up to engaging in that activity each day for a week.

Self-care doesn't have to be complicated! Here are some suggestions to help you start your self-care journey slowly:

- **Get frequent exercise:** Walking for 30 minutes daily can help you feel better and healthier. If you can't do 30 minutes, start with 10. Even small quantities of activity add up. You can even try breaking it up by walking 10 minutes during your lunch break and 10 minutes after work. Do a gentle five-minute stretch in the morning and just before going to bed.
- **Eat frequent, nutritious meals and drink plenty of water:** Maintaining mental and physical performance with the help of a healthy diet and lots of water is possible. Also, avoid drinking too much coffee or other caffeinated drinks, as this messes with your sleep cycle and hormone production.
- **Make sleep a top priority:** Maintain a routine and ensure you receive sufficient sleep. Try to limit your screen time in the hours leading up to bedtime. It is even more important to prioritize your sleep cycle if you're a parent who struggles with the rigors of little to no sleep while caring for newborns or toddlers. We all need sleep to function properly—that means you, too, Mom!

- **Take up a calming activity:** Explore relaxation or wellness apps or programs, including breathing techniques, meditation, or both. These healthy hobbies, as well as any others you love, like writing, should have regular times. Make it a priority to schedule your downtime!
- **Establish priorities and goals:** Determine what needs to be done right away versus what can wait. If you feel you are taking on too much, practice saying "no" to new projects. When the day is over, focus on your successes rather than your shortcomings.
- **Be thankful:** Every day, remind yourself of your blessings. Be specific about what you are grateful for. At night, jot these things down or play them again in your head.
- **Think positively:** Recognize your negative ideas and combat them.
- **Stay connected with loved ones:** Get in touch with people you know who will be there for you when things become hard.

Self-care can improve health and mindset, but only if you want to invest in yourself. Each person can choose self-care as a proactive means of caring for their well-being.

What Is Self-Love?

Self-love is a feeling of admiration for yourself that develops through behaviors encouraging mental, emotional, and spiritual development. It means placing a high value on your health and happiness and attending to your needs rather than putting your health at risk to please others. Accepting nothing less than what you deserve is a sign of self-love.

Since we all have a variety of methods to care for ourselves, self-love can mean various things to different people. A crucial aspect of maintaining your mental health is determining what self-love means to you personally.

Let's look at some ways in which you can express self-love.

Do Not Compare Yourself to Others

Comparing ourselves to others comes naturally since we are socialized to be competitive. However, this can be dangerous. There is only one *you* in the entire universe, so it's silly to compare your uniqueness to anyone else. Instead, pay attention to yourself and your path. Simply shifting your energy can help you feel liberated.

Don't Be Concerned With What Others Think

Don't worry about what people think of you or what they *might* think of you if you express yourself honestly or attempt XYZ. You are free to be you. You can only please some people, therefore trying to please everyone is a huge waste of time and energy. Do not let others hold you back from reaching your full potential. Take that opportunity, start that new hobby or side hustle, and be who you've always wanted to be.

Permit Yourself to Make Errors

We're told from an early age that "nobody's perfect," and everyone makes mistakes somewhere along the line. Still, the pressure to succeed only increases as you get older. We need to make mistakes, however, if we want to learn and grow from them. To grow from where you find yourself in the present moment, you also need to accept your past. You're continually evolving from the person you were yesterday into who you are now and who you will be tomorrow.

So ignore that inner voice that tells you that you have to be flawless. Make plenty of errors! It's what you learn from your mistakes that matters.

Get Rid of Toxic Individuals

Everybody emits energy into this world, but only some accept responsibility for who they are. If someone in your life is displaying toxic behavior and refuses to take responsibility for it, then you may need to distance yourself from them. Even if it is unpleasant to tell them why you need to take a step back, it is freeing and necessary. Remember to protect your energy at all costs.

Have Faith in Your Ability to Make Sound Judgments for Yourself

Although we usually have a good sense of what is best for us, we tend to second-guess ourselves and question our abilities. Keep in mind that your emotions are valid. Be your best ally since you are the only one who truly understands *you*.

Seize Any Opportunity That Comes Your Way

The timing of your next significant step in life will always be challenging, and sometimes unexpected. The setup may be flawed, but it should allow you to achieve your objectives and aspirations. If something moves your heart and feels right, take advantage of the opportunity, as it might not come around again.

Prioritize Yourself

You need to put yourself first, and *no*, you shouldn't feel awful about it. Women, in particular, tend to develop a habit of putting others first, but we also need to set aside some time to unwind. Otherwise, if you don't take time to recharge, you end up putting a lot of strain on yourself, which can easily lead to stress and anxiety. Set aside time to do what you're passionate about each day. Find activities that bring you joy and do more of them. This will nourish your soul.

Extend Your Capacity to Feel Both Sorrow and Joy

Allow yourself to experience all your emotions truly and to their full extent. Don't place boundaries around your emotions, and embrace both your joy and your sadness. Similar to how fear may help you understand yourself, grief and joy can also lead you to the realization that you are not your emotions; you are merely experiencing them.

Be Brave

Make it a practice to express yourself honestly. The more you practice boldness, the more it grows and easier it becomes. Be sure to settle in at the table without asking for approval. Participate in the discussions that matter to you. Please share your ideas—someone needs to hear them! Take the initiative and remember that your voice matters as much as anyone else's.

Find Beauty in the Simplest of Things

Make an effort to admire at least one lovely, tiny detail every day. Make a mental note of it and be thankful for it. Gratitude not only provides perspective, but it is also necessary for finding joy. Even if you don't feel particularly happy at that moment, take a second to consider how far you've come and how much you've survived. You are present now, living and capable of things you can't even imagine. Be kind to yourself in the process.

Why Self-Love Heals Anxiety: A Personal Choice

There are several main reasons for anxiety, which are all connected to different types of self-abandonment. Below is a list of the types of self-abandonment and how each one relates to your anxiety.

Emotional Self-Abandonment and Anxiety

A sobbing infant or young child will feel lonely, abandoned, and worried if you neglect them. Your inner child experiences the same sentiments when you dismiss or criticize your emotions! Anxiety is how our inner child communicates when we do not love ourselves, but instead, abandon ourselves. Anxiety tells you, "I'm afraid, and I feel rejected whenever you are not here for me—when you ignore me, or you attempt to numb your thoughts with addictions, or even when you make someone else accountable for your feelings. I feel uneasy and under pressure when you criticize me and think that I'm not good enough."

When you experience anxiety or any emotion other than inner calm and fulfillment, you could practice what some experts call *Inner Bonding*, or self-love. This refers to how you show yourself emotional love and acceptance—a vital factor in healing from anxiety. In some cases related to childhood trauma or abuse, it can be extremely difficult to move past the emotional entrapment brought on by these experiences and show ourselves the love we all need. In fact, putting off our healing journey is a type of self-abandonment. If moving beyond this is too much for you to handle on your own, that's okay. I suggest seeking the help of a qualified professional who specializes in deeper emotional healing, because you deserve to fall in love with yourself.

Physical Self-Abandonment and Anxiety

Anxiety can result from brain poisoning, which is caused by a gut flora imbalance. You reduce your good gut flora while supporting opportunistic harmful bacteria when you ingest factory-farmed, processed foods and use different medicines. The vagus nerve, the longest and one of our most important nerves, then transports the toxins in your intestines to your brain. Your brain is your most important ally when it pertains to stabilizing your anxiety levels and keeping a healthy mind.

You may also experience anxiety if you are not drinking enough clean water or if you are eating sweets and carbohydrates late at night, which may result in low blood sugar. Anxiety results from the adrenaline released when we lack sufficient water or our blood sugar levels are too low to ensure the brain gets what it needs.

Learning how to nourish your body through diet, exercise, rest, and hydration is essential to self-love.

Financial Self-Abandonment and Anxiety

You'll probably experience anxiety when you splurge and put your finances in danger, or when you are so frugal that you deny yourself the chance to enjoy life. This can happen when you become fixated on money and let your wounded self terrify you about the future.

Making sure you have enough income to meet your requirements, avoiding credit card debt, allowing yourself to enjoy life when you have enough money, and focusing on the here and now rather than constantly worrying about the future are all examples of loving yourself financially.

Organizational Self-Abandonment and Anxiety

Anxiety is likely to arise from chronic lateness, procrastination, and excessive clutter. Learning to love yourself requires being a grownup in handling your time and space, instead of letting your reluctant, wounded self run the show.

Relational Self-Abandonment and Anxiety

Anxiety is typical among those who give themselves over to people-pleasing or surrender their vulnerable "inner child" to someone in hopes that they will provide a secure environment for them. Anxiety might develop when you rely on others to give you the care you should be giving yourself.

Speaking the truth in a relationship requires compassionately disengaging in order to care for yourself afterward, either to learn from the dispute or to love yourself more deeply. To properly embrace people and love yourself, however, you must first accept yourself completely. Being kind to yourself and others is an important part of loving yourself.

Spiritual Self-Abandonment and Anxiety

Feeling nervous and alone is a sign that you are closing yourself off from your higher power and the love, compassion, knowledge, and strength you need to take good care of yourself.

Practicing self-love on a spiritual level entails learning to keep your heart and mind open. It means connecting to your higher guidance, whether for you that be God, nature, or the universe, so that you may tend to your needs with compassion, humility, and wisdom.

When you learn to love yourself instead of continuing to abandon yourself in all of these ways—emotionally, physically, financially, organizationally, relationally, and spiritually—you will experience feelings of peace and fullness instead of anxiety.

Chapter 4:

Eat, Exercise, Energize, Repeat

It is possible to control anxiety through methods that make you feel less tense immediately and over time. Many things influence your mental health, including how you care for your body, what you eat, how you breathe, and how consistent you are in the long run.

Here are some suggestions for enhancing your mental health with four easy-to-follow steps to incorporate into your daily routine.

Step 1: Eat

Are there foods that help us reduce anxiety? Studies have revealed that although some meals might briefly function as stimulants, others can help us feel calmer (Orenstein, 2018). Making certain dietary changes can assist if you encounter stress that causes anxiety or panic attacks.

Here are a few ideas:

- Try eating more complex carbohydrates like oats, potatoes, beans, which the body can convert into the feel-good neurotransmitter serotonin. Choose whole grain cereals and bread instead of sweet snacks or drinks.
- To maintain stable blood sugar levels and to give yourself energy, eat protein like eggs, yogurt, cheese, nut butter, or protein shakes at breakfast.
- Stay hydrated. Mood swings may start to surface as a result of dehydration.

Consider including the following in your diet to improve your mood:

- dark chocolate
- vegetables like artichokes, kale, spinach, beets, broccoli
- folic acid with additional B vitamins
- low-glycemic index foods that absorb sugar slowly and convert more efficiently to fuel, such as apples, berries, cherries, sourdough bread, coconut sugar

- magnesium
- fatty acids (omega-3)
- nuts like walnuts, pecans, and cashews
- mineral-rich herbal teas such as chamomile, nettle, and raspberry leaf. These are also a great way to stay hydrated!

Research published in August 2015 in the journal *Psychiatry Research* indicated that eating probiotic-rich foods can help reduce social anxiety. **Kefir, kebabs, and fermented foods like pickles and sauerkraut are all great sources of probiotics** (Orenstein, 2018). Probiotics have been associated with reducing the symptoms of major depressive disorder, according to a recent study released in 2017 in the journal *Annals of General Psychiatry*. This association may be due to probiotics boosting serotonin levels and reducing inflammation in the body.

What to Eat

If you need a bit more guidance on what to eat to reduce your anxiety, have a look at the following:

Foods High in Tryptophan

Tryptophan is an amino acid that is a precursor of serotonin, a neurotransmitter that promotes relaxation. Because tryptophan helps your brain create feel-good neurotransmitters, some researchers think it may be able to reduce stress.

Foods that contain tryptophan include eggs, turkey, chicken, bananas, milk, oats, cheese, and peanut butter.

It should be noted that it is unclear if tryptophan present in food passes the blood-brain barrier, therefore the impact might not be as strong as taking tryptophan supplements, for example.

Beef and Vitamin B-Rich Foods Reduce Anxiety

Thiamine, often known as vitamin B1, is one of the B vitamins linked in research to improved mental health. Some people may get depressed if they don't get enough B vitamins like folic acid and B12. Anxiety can be avoided using vitamin B supplements or meals high in B vitamins.

Foods that contain thiamine include beef, pork, chicken, lentils, citrus fruits, rice, almonds, and eggs.

Complex Carbohydrates Are Mood-Boosting Foods

Serotonin synthesis in the brain is also boosted by carbohydrates. Whole grains release sugar into circulation gradually because they take longer for the body to break them down. While consuming processed carbohydrates may provide you with a temporary boost of energy, it is often followed by a sudden loss in energy when your blood sugar levels caused by the insulin rush lower dramatically.

Instead of processed options like sugar, sweets, white bread, and white rice, **choose whole grains like whole-wheat bread or brown rice for mood-enhancing carbohydrates.**

Include Foods High in Omega-3s

Omega-3 fatty acids are found in fatty fish like salmon, tuna, lake trout, herring, anchovies, and sardines.

Foods High in Protein Can Help You Stay Alert

Norepinephrine and dopamine are brain chemicals that, like serotonin, act as neurotransmitters to convey signals between nerve cells. Norepinephrine and higher dopamine levels increase alertness, mental vigor, and response speed, and protein helps to boost their synthesis. A combination of complex carbs and protein, spaced throughout the day, is great for mood enhancement.

Some excellent sources of protein include Greek yogurt, wild fish, grass-fed meats, organic eggs, cheese, almonds, beans, soy, and lentils.

What to Avoid

Here is a list of foods that would be better to avoid if you feel anxious:

Caffeinated Beverages

Some individuals frequently consume meals high in sugar, caffeine, and other stimulants when they need an energy boost. While binging on sweets may temporarily increase your serotonin levels, coffee lowers serotonin levels in the brain, and you could feel irritated and depressed when your serotonin levels are low. Additionally, as a diuretic, caffeine causes frequent visits to the toilet, too much of which may lead to dehydration—another factor that can lead to depression. Caffeine might also keep you awake, which can lead to worry and anxiety. Remember that getting enough sleep is essential for a good mood.

Sweets

Everyone enjoys something sweet from time to time. Sugary foods, such as those made with corn syrup or table sugar, give us a quick rush of energy but are more destructive to our health than anything else. They can be a culprit in accelerating our anxiety due to being highly processed in nature and our body's inability to process them. As the rush quickly fades away, your insulin production rises to flush the sugar from your system. Then you start experiencing symptoms of fatigue and depression and need more sugar to obtain that same feeling! Sugar is your body's primary source of fuel ("How to Heal Your Metabolism with Kate Deering," 2021), so be sure to consume good sugar from natural sources such as honey, organic cane sugar, and coconut sugar paired with protein to avoid crashing and to keep your mood stable.

Alcohol

Alcohol reduces tension and anxiety for certain people. Unfortunately, the positive "effect" is short-lived and fleeting. The fact is that alcohol has a long-term depressive effect. It is considered a diuretic like coffee and quickly dehydrates the body, which we know is not conducive to improving your mood or overall health.

Processed Foods

Could consuming processed foods like hot dogs, sausages, pies, and cakes make you feel anxious later on? According to researchers in London, a diet high in processed and fatty foods raises the risk of depression (Orenstein, 2018). Results showed that compared to individuals who ate "whole" meals including fish and vegetables, those whose diets were mainly fried and contained processed meat, high-fat dairy items, and sugary sweets had a 58% greater risk of depression. Skip the overly processed meals if you want to improve your mood.

If it is accessible and you can afford it, strongly consider trying to implement more sustainable food choices such as organic meats and vegetables. Eating locally not only means consuming healthier quality food—there is something ancestral about knowing where your food comes from and being more connected to it. When you know what kind of diet the chicken you are eating has had, you know what kind of nutrients you are putting into your body as well. And let's not forget that eating locally supports small businesses, which is also good for the soul!

Step 2: Exercise

Try one or more of the following techniques to get some control over your feelings whenever and wherever you feel anxious. These physical activities will enable you to unwind rapidly.

The word "exercise" sometimes puts people off because it sounds like something difficult to achieve or be consistent with. *How can I make time for exercise when I barely have time for everything else in my life?* Rest assured: it may not be as difficult as you think to incorporate movement into your life. Humans were designed to move, and we thrive when our bodies get regular use through physical interaction. Exercise naturally regulates our bodily functions, emotions, and the chemistry in our brain by releasing feel-good hormones like dopamine, serotonin, and oxytocin—all of which directly combat anxiety.

Incorporating exercise into your routine does not mean you have to get a membership at a gym or invest in expensive equipment to use at home. All you really have to do is simply activate your muscles and move your body in a way that feels good to you. For instance, my preferred way to get out negative or anxious energy is to crank up the music and dance it out in my living room. Sometimes, after dinner, I just take off for a brisk walk around the block. And yes, both of these habits are considered beneficial exercise. Anything that gets your body moving in a way that feels comfortable, natural, and even enjoyable can be transformed into an exercise routine.

You might consider biking (which is fun and adventurous), simple stretching, yoga, jogging, or lifting weights with things around your house (like your kids). Be creative and find something you enjoy. Incorporating these small habits that work for you can not only be a practice of regulating your energy, but also a vital act of self-care. Find your preferred method to move your body and do it whenever you start to feel tense or out of control.

While physical exercise and all kinds of movement are vital for getting our positive emotions and energies flowing, you can optimize their effects by incorporating deep breathing exercises, too.

Breathe Deeply to Relax

You may notice that your breathing and pulse rate quicken when you feel nervous, and you could start to perspire and experience lightheadedness or dizziness. Taking control of your breathing might help you feel calmer when stressed.

When you're worried, do these actions to manage your breathing:

- **Find a peaceful spot to sit and feel at ease.** Position your hands so that one is on your tummy and the other is on your chest. When you take a deep breath in, you should feel the movement in your stomach more than your chest.
- **Inhale deeply through your nose,** allowing the air to fill your diaphragm and cause your stomach to rise. Wait a few seconds, then exhale slowly through your mouth, bringing your navel to your spine as you do so. As you breathe, pay attention to your hands moving. You should notice the hand resting on your stom-

ach moving as your stomach fills with air during your inhale. The hand on your chest however, will have little to no movement.

- **Do this at least ten times,** or until you feel the effects of the exercise and your worry begins to subside.

Use Your Imagination

Have you heard the phrase "finding your happy place?" Your body and mind might become more relaxed if you visualize a relaxing environment.

When your anxiety starts to rise, find yourself a calm spot to let your imagination wander. Consider where you would want to unwind—although it might be anywhere in the world, actual or imagined, it has to be a scene that makes you feel incredibly comfortable, content, and tranquil. To refer to it later on in the future when you have anxiety, make sure it is simple enough to visualize.

Imagine all the minute details you'd discover if you were actually there. Imagine the environment's aroma, ambiance, and sound. Imagine yourself there, relaxed and taking it all in.

My happy place? Near the ocean or in a forest, depending on how I feel that day. But I love nothing more than imagining the ocean waves crashing gently onto the shore, with a slightly misty breeze in the air, the warm rays of the sun on my face, and the refreshing smell of salt water.

Once you have a clear mental image of your happy place, shut your eyes and focus on breathing normally and slowly through your nose while exhaling through your mouth. Do this for a few minutes. Keep your attention on your breathing and keep picturing your happy place until you feel your nervousness easing. Anytime you have anxiety, return to this location in your thoughts.

Remain Calm by Counting

It's easy to reduce your worry by counting. With your eyes closed, breathe deeply and gently count to 10. Count to 20, or even more if you have to. Count until you start to sense a decrease in anxiousness.

The feeling of relief usually appears instantly, but it might also take some time. Maintain patience and calm, and you'll find that counting takes your mind off of your tension. It's an excellent technique to use in a busy or people-packed environment, like on a bus, a train, or in a store, where it would be more challenging to carry out other anxiety exercises.

You can teach yourself how to relax. It requires practice, much like physical exercise or anything else in life. Keep trying alternative workouts or techniques until you find one that works for you.

Let Your Muscles Relax

When you experience anxiety, your muscles may feel strained or tense, too. Help yourself relax by doing the following:

- Find a peaceful spot to sit and feel at ease.
- Focus on your breathing while closing your eyes. Slowly inhale through your nose and exhale through your mouth.
- Clench your hand into a fist.
- For a few seconds, keep your hand clenched. Take note of the tightness in your hand.
- Open your fingers gradually and pay attention to your feelings. You could feel your hand releasing the stress, and it will eventually feel looser and lighter.
- Continue contracting and then relaxing your hands, legs, shoulders, feet, and other muscle groups throughout your body. Alternating between tensing and relaxing each set of muscles might be helpful.

PMR: Progressive Muscle Relaxation

Progressive muscle relaxation (PMR) takes the previous exercise to the next level. Anyone suffering from anxiety, sleeplessness, or any other emotionally distressing ailment might benefit from this simple yet effective practice (Star, 2019). PMR is a relaxation method, much like yoga, visualization, and breathing techniques. It can even help anyone overcome a panic attack, and is especially useful during times of extreme stress or anxiety.

In the 1920s, American doctor Edmund Jacobson initially tested PMR on his patients. Regardless of their disease, Jacobson observed that most of the people he examined had muscular tension and discomfort.

When he advised them to unwind, he noticed that most individuals didn't appear connected and conscious enough of their bodily stress to release it.

Jacobson used this new realization as motivation to create a series of processes for contracting, then releasing a set of muscles. He discovered that by doing so, his patients could better recognize the sensation of tension, which taught them what it means to let it go and experience a state of relaxation.

The method has undergone several modifications since then. Still, they are all based on Jacobson's original concept of sequentially contracting and then relaxing certain muscle groups.

The relaxation response, which lowers heart rate, calms the mind, and releases physical stress, is elicited by relaxation techniques like PMR.

Another benefit of PMR is that it might make someone more conscious of the connection between their bodily stress and mental condition. One can release nervous thoughts and sensations by relaxing their body.

Step-By-Step PMR

The cornerstone of PMR is this meticulous technique of building and releasing tension all over your body. It is possible to quiet and relax the mind while relieving physical tension by methodically contracting and releasing different muscle groups.

Here are the instructions for a simple PMR that anybody can complete:

Step 1

Sit down and relax. PMR may be performed while sitting up in a chair; you do not need to lie down to perform it. Do your best to eliminate any interruptions. If it makes you feel better, close your eyes.

Step 2

Breathe deeply, as we saw in the previous section.

Step 3

Starting with the feet, tense and then relax your muscles. Clench your toes while pointing your heels downward. For a few breaths, squeeze firmly, then let go. Then, stretch your feet inward while pointing your toes toward your head. Hold for a short while and let go.

Step 4

Next, tighten and release your calf muscles, then your thighs. Each muscle group should be tightened and released as you progress through your body. Start from the bottom and work your way up, ending with your face. Try to tense each muscle group for a couple of breaths, and then gently let go. Any regions that seem particularly rigid should be repeated until you notice a difference.

Step 5

Now, take a few deep breaths and pay attention to how you feel.

PMR is a skill that requires practice to perfect. To learn what it feels like to be at ease, practice PMR regularly, especially when you're not under pressure to use it. That way, you'll know what to expect when you truly need it—that is, when you're facing a challenging or anxiety-inducing circumstance.

Step 3: Energize

Essential oils are fragrant liquids derived from plants, blossoms, and fruits. According to research, using certain essential oils in aromatherapy may aid anxiety relief and promote relaxation (Nall, 2019).

Aromatherapy

Aromatic oils are released when plants are steamed or pressed. The flavor and aroma of the plants are present in these oils, and the essence of a plant is a common term for these components. Products like candles, perfumes, and aromatherapy smells can all include "essences."

It's important to note that many traditional candles and fragrances in stores are not the same as the natural plant essences created from premium essential oils. Artificial candles, perfumes, and scents are endocrine disruptors that have a negative impact on our bodies' health. They won't have the same therapeutic benefits as essential oils. When deciding which essential oils to use, it is critical to expand your knowledge of how they were created in the first place.

The History

Historically, aromatherapy has its roots in eastern medicinal methods that are thousands of years old. Resins, balms, and oils containing aromatic plant components were widely used as therapies for various health ailments in ancient China, India, Egypt, and other cultures.

In recent years, essential oils have been increasingly appreciated as non-conventional remedies all over the world. The health community is also becoming more aware of the benefits of natural medicine, including plants and their oils.

How Does Aromatherapy Work?

When essential oils release an essence that makes us feel good, it is known as aromatherapy. Natural plant extracts are used in this holistic therapeutic method to support certain aspects of our health. Aromatherapy, sometimes referred to as essential oil treatment, employs medicinally compelling aromatic essential oils to enrich our physical, mental, and spiritual well-being.

Aromatherapy is regarded as both a science and an art. The ability of a fragrance to elicit vivid memories demonstrates aromatherapy's effectiveness. You feel better when you recall the enticing aroma of your early childhood, such as freshly baked cinnamon cookies at your grandmother's home. Some aromas, like those of springtime, tend to have a more therapeutic effect, though the effects of various fragrances might differ from one person to the next, depending on their connection to the smell. You may feel more energized by some scents, like lemon, while other citrus fruits, like orange or grapefruit, are effective if you feel worn out and sad.

Which Essential Oils Are Effective for Reducing Anxiety?

Essential oils can help calm nerves and improve your mood. Among these essential oils are:

- lavender
- frankincense
- orange bergamot
- grapefruit
- mandarin
- lime
- lemon
- lemongrass
- chamomile
- basil
- clary sage
- peppermint
- geranium
- tea tree
- sandalwood
- rose
- rosemary
- neroli
- ylang-ylang
- sweet orange
- vetiver

Tips for Using Essential Oils

Essential oils are exceptionally pure and potent. That being said, it is important to understand how to properly use them and be aware that some oils should not be consumed as they may have toxic and adverse effects. Make sure you understand how to use the oils you choose to work with.

Similarly, many oils may need to be diluted with different carrier oils before becoming safe to apply on the skin. To dilute the essential oil, use a carrier oil such as coconut, olive, or jojoba. Make sure to always read the instructions on the label before using.

It's also a good idea to run a patch test of the essential oil on skin or clothing, just in case. Some might discolor, irritate the skin, or trigger an allergic response. It's best to avoid these oils altogether.

Using diluted essential oils can be done in a variety of ways, including:

- putting it in specific diffusers
- rubbing it into the skin by using it as massage oil (always use a carrier oil for this!)
- adding it to lotions or bath salts and having a steam bath

- having the scent somewhere in your car to relax your nerves while driving
- putting it on your jewelry (if it is safe to do so)
- applying it to textiles and soft furnishings, such as your blankets or pillows

Deep Breathing Exercises With Essential Oils

As seen in an earlier section, taking slow, deep breaths sends the message to your body that you're calm and in command. This is among the simplest methods to achieve inner calm, as deep breathing helps to lower cortisol levels, soothes the body, and controls heart rate.

Deep breathing becomes automatic when you do it frequently, so I advise arranging breathing breaks throughout your day. I like taking mine during my lunch hour; it serves as a little pick-me-up when I'm feeling low or stressed throughout the day. I find that when I make time for deep breathing, it allows me to recenter myself to carry on with the rest of my day.

The technique for including essential oils into your deep breathing ritual is as follows:

- Choose your preferred essential oil for this time (lavender and sandalwood work wonders to calm the mind!). Keep the oil nearby in a diffuser or aromatherapy stick.
- Position yourself comfortably and focus on your breathing.
- Start by slowly taking 10 breaths.
- Inhale deeply through your nose while counting to five. Feel the air rush into your lungs.
- Take a gentle pause, holding your breath for five seconds, and then slowly let it out to the count of five.

Aromatherapy works because your mind is diverted from the irritation or tension you feel when you inhale that aroma. As you inhale deeply, you lose yourself in the moment and enjoy the soothing aroma (*Stressed Out? Aromatherapy Can Help You to Feel Calmer*, 2015).

Step 4: Repeat

Consistency is essential in many aspects of life, and personal wellness is one of them. Not sure how consistency can make a difference?

Take regular exercise as an example. Even in small doses, regular exercise is more beneficial than occasional high-intensity workouts. It is important to approach mental health the same way. It would be best if you were consistent with your efforts.

Consider your daily habits for a moment. Do you have a routine set in place? Routines can help us build mental toughness. And even though you would gain significantly from doing so, you do not need to practice these new strategies nonstop. Doing them as required from time to time would also benefit you greatly.

Small and simple acts can significantly influence your life and how you go about it, so start small and work your way up. Make your bed when you get up. Eat a healthy breakfast and practice excellent hygiene. Schedule time for exercise, meditation, and sleep—and don't forget to take a break now and again! It's time to prioritize your mental health and make it a point to check in with yourself frequently.

Chapter 5:

You Are a Queen, and This Is Your Kingdom

It is important to establish and maintain healthy boundaries to enjoy a safe environment in any relationship. Likewise, boundary-setting is essential for your well-being and keeping your anxiety levels at bay.

Boundaries are mediated by your culture, personality, and social setting, all of which play a significant role. When you're among old friends in a nightclub, for example, the boundaries are very different from the ones you have at work in a professional meeting with your colleagues! In all types of relationships, setting boundaries clarifies our expectations of ourselves and others.

Boundaries

In their simplest form, boundaries are the limits or borders that set you apart from others. Our skin is the most visible of our many borders. Still, we also have limits in our interpersonal interactions that go beyond our bodies.

In western society, many of us are taught from an early age to adapt and shape ourselves to the comfort of others. Because of this, we often find it challenging to establish our own limits as we get older—even when doing so would ultimately harm us, we want to avoid offending other people. We are taught to put others' needs before our own, and as a result, we need to relearn what limits are and how we can set them.

Setting boundaries is essential for:

- preserving your self-respect and sense of power
- a feeling of self-worth
- experiencing fulfillment in your relationships
- juggling your demands with those of other people
- getting what you want and need
- having a sense of balance and control over your life
- general happiness

Personal Boundaries

The boundaries we set for ourselves about our comfort with and around others are called personal boundaries.

These boundaries might be related to:

- physical touch, for example, not feeling at ease giving a stranger a hug
- verbal communication, like not wanting a friend or family member to speak down to you
- public interaction, including choosing to keep strangers out of your personal space

Boundaries can also exist in several settings, such as when visiting relatives, at work, at home, or when out with friends. Whether or not we choose to share our "comfort zones" with others, the fact remains that we all have them. But if we don't express our limits, they are more likely to be crossed.

Why Is It Crucial to Establish Healthy Boundaries?

Each of us has unique limits and lines that help us better navigate life and interpersonal interactions. But every boundary is different, and few can accurately predict another individual's limits.

Simply stating your needs for constructive connection with others is the essence of setting limits. Not everyone may appreciate or understand your boundaries or the reasons behind them. But at the same time, you can't expect others to respect your limits if you don't know what these are or if you don't set them yourself.

Self-awareness is necessary for setting healthy limits. It's important to be honest with yourself and upfront about what you want from others, as well as what you're willing to tolerate and what you're not. Clear and assertive communication skills are necessary for establishing appropriate limits.

As a type of self-care, setting healthy boundaries necessitates being assertive about your needs and priorities. While expressing your emotions respectfully and transparently does not imply making demands, it does call on others to pay attention to your needs. Adults may have been taught that expressing their wants is wrong and selfish by the people who nurtured them as children. Setting good boundaries as an adult can be difficult, but avoiding that discomfort can lead to something even worse: relationships marked by bitterness, manipulation, and abuse.

Types of Boundaries

Consider the areas where you're having issues as a starting point for identifying your limits. Do you frequently feel worn out? Do you feel uneasy about coworkers? Do your mother's invasions make you angry? These issues indicate that you lack limits in this particular area of your life. Let's take a look at the different kinds of boundaries we may need to set.

Physical

Your right to be left alone, your sense of privacy, and your ability to take care of basic bodily requirements, like eating and sleeping, are all protected by having boundaries in place. They communicate to others what degree of physical contact is acceptable, how much privacy you require, and how to behave in your personal space. A physical barrier clearly defines your body and personal space as being yours.

Here are some examples:

- You step away or excuse yourself if someone sits too close to you and explain, "I need a bit more personal space."
- You don't use or keep alcohol in your home, therefore you prefer not to be in the presence of people who choose to drink it.

Sexual

Your right to sexual consent, to request the kinds of sex you want, and to be open about your partner's sexual past are all protected by sexual boundaries. They specify the type, frequency, timing, location, and partner of the sex you desire.

Here are some examples:

- "I want to be touched in this way."
- "I prefer to avoid engaging in sexual activity right now."

Emotional

Your right to have your ideas and feelings, to not have them judged or rejected, and to not be required to consider the feelings of others are all protected by emotional or mental boundaries. Maintaining healthy emotional boundaries means taking responsibility for your emotions while recognizing that you cannot control the emotions of those around you. By respecting one another's feelings and refraining from the intimate oversharing of details unsuitable for the kind or degree of intimacy in the relationship, emotional boundaries also help us establish a sense of emotional safety.

Here are some examples:

- "I'm not sure how to talk about this."
- "When you criticize me in the presence of our children, I feel ashamed and helpless. Please stop talking to me in that manner and tone."

Religious or Spiritual

Physical and psychological limits safeguard people's freedom to freely practice their religion or spirituality and their right to freely worship and express their views. You should never be scrutinized for wanting to engage in practices that help you feel uplifted, connected, and balanced.

Here are some examples:

- "Before we eat, I will pause and offer a silent prayer."
- You attend church alone since your spouse doesn't have the same beliefs as you.

Material and Financial Limits

Financial and material boundaries safeguard your right to control how you spend your money, to withhold your money or property from giving or lending if you so desire, and to be compensated by an employer following the terms of the contract.

Here are some examples:

- "I didn't join you out for lunch today because I'm on a tight budget and packed my own."
- "Please only take my car after asking me."

Your Time

Time restrictions safeguard how you use your free time. They protect you from overcommitting yourself, being pressured into doing things you don't want to, and having other people squander your time.

Here are some examples:

- "My evenings are set aside for family time. I'll reply to all business emails in the morning."
- "I don't have time to take you shopping this week, Mom. I'll order some groceries from the supermarket delivery service on your behalf."

Non-Negotiable Boundaries

Some limits can never be lowered, and these include things you can't live without in order to feel secure. These concerns typically involve threats to your physical or mental well-being, addiction to drugs or alcohol, infidelity, or severe health conditions.

Here are some examples:

- "Mom, my kids won't be allowed to visit your house if you don't have a fence around your pool."
- "If my partner cheats on me, it will end the relationship since I see adultery as a deal-breaker."

I advise you to put your boundaries in writing to make yourself accountable for setting these limits and protecting yourself. Make sure you spend your time, attention, and resources on the things that are most important to you.

Barriers to Boundaries

What barriers hinder us from determining our boundaries?

Possible barriers include:

- fear of being rejected or abandoned
- fear of conflict and offending someone
- shame or guilt
- lack of knowledge

Our preconceived notions about relationships often serve to reinforce these obstacles to setting limits. These misconceptions and emotions complicate the boundary-setting process and may even prevent us from accomplishing it.

Removing obstacles is a crucial component in establishing limits. But first, it's critical to recognize what your obstacles are. Look into the myths that are getting in your way, and notice if you speak to yourself in the following ways:

- *My wants are not as significant as those of other people.*
- *If they don't want to help me, it's because I'm asking too much of them.*
- *It is selfish to ask for this boundary.*
- *Needing this limit reveals my weakness.*
- *I am accountable for the other person's feelings.*

Removing obstacles to setting limits involves challenging these ideas and misconceptions by asking yourself, *Are these things I am telling myself actually true? What evidence do I have to prove that they are true?* You might just find that you can debunk yourself from being one of your own obstacles right then and there. If you do this, you'll be better able to control the feelings of regret, guilt, and fear that keep you from achieving your goals. You will be able to establish and enforce boundaries more easily from then on.

How To Overcome Obstacles to Establishing Boundaries

- **Determine what your obstacles are.** Pinpoint precisely what is preventing you from speaking up for yourself.
- **Examine your reasoning for believing these myths to be real.** Consider what experiences prompted you to hold these myths in high regard. Take into account how your personal experiences and the opinions of others have shaped your perspective on creating boundaries. Did the individuals in your life directly or indirectly tell you about these myths? Have you tried setting limits in the past and had bad results? Is there a general lack of self-worth, which makes it challenging to be proactive about meeting your needs?
- **Take the falsehoods on by reminding yourself of the real facts instead.** For instance, convince yourself that you deserve to acquire what you want rather than telling yourself that you don't! Reviewing your myth challenges on a daily basis might be useful so that the next time you contemplate establishing a limit, you'll be better prepared to handle the inevitable challenges you'll face.
- **Stop predicting the worst.** Usually, the feared outcome of creating a limit is worse than the actual outcome. It is simple to overthink the implications and potential solutions. Determine what you're afraid of. How plausible is the outcome or reaction, in your opinion? How horrible would it be if it did happen, and how would you handle it? This will remind you that you can achieve your goals without confrontation and that, even when things don't go your way, you have the strength to handle them.

Boundaries for Different Social Situations

Setting boundaries is crucial, but it may be challenging. Many people need to gain the skills necessary to express their needs to others, or even to know where to start. Suppose you're trying to figure out how to establish your limits. In that case, it could be a good idea to start by considering the kind of boundary you want to create.

Emotional

These boundaries define how emotionally accessible you are to others. Everybody needs support from time to time when life throws us a curveball or when we need assistance processing little stresses that occur throughout the day (Selva, 2018).

We can't constantly be there for others, though, since we frequently need to take care of other obligations like jobs, household chores, and family commitments. And as responsible adults, we need to put ourselves first from time to time. As you now know, self-care is the cornerstone of wellness. Codependency, characterized by placing others' needs before our own, can sometimes create anxiety and even result in burnout.

The inability to set and enforce limits with others can lead to resentment, remorse, and exhaustion. If someone puts excessive demands on your emotional resources, it's completely acceptable to let them know your limits. Suppose they resist your limits or keep breaking them. In that case, your connection may be unhealthy, troublesome, or even toxic.

Establishing Emotional Boundaries

We don't always consciously think to create emotional boundaries until after they've been broken, and they usually have to do with how people speak to or treat us.

Imagine that you had a disagreement with someone and you called each other names. The easiest method to establish an emotional barrier with them when you have both cooled down is to:

- approach them and ask to discuss the disagreement
- own up to whatever role you may have had in the conflict
- inform them that you will not tolerate name-calling and expect them to engage in conversation in the future without going to that extreme

Everyone has the right to state their preferences and refusals without having to justify or explain themselves. Still, having a relationship with someone we can't get away from, like a family member or coworker, can be challenging. There may be a need to alter the dynamics of a relationship altogether when one party frequently violates another's limits.

At Work

Establishing and maintaining appropriate workplace boundaries has become more challenging with the rise of remote and hybrid workplaces and rapid technological advancement.

When interviewing for a new job, you must be clear about your expectations for things like accessibility during business hours, out-of-office work, and telecommuting.

Here are some suggestions for creating appropriate boundaries at work:

- Express yourself clearly. Be honest but also professional. Avoid participating in conversations between coworkers about one another.
- You may establish clear working frameworks by letting your coworkers know when you don't want to be interrupted, especially when you need to concentrate.
- Keep all of your interactions professional. While it could be alluring, developing close friendships with coworkers might result in conflicts and blurred boundaries.
- To manage your workload, assign tasks to others.
- Take a break.
- Keep people in the loop and use collaborative project management software like Trello or Asana to establish and stick to your work hours.

Friendships

It takes trust and respect between friends to establish and uphold limits. These can also alter when life events that cause a priority change occur. For instance, after establishing a family, you could adjust how much time and effort you devote to your connections. And if you have kids, your children's needs take precedence over those of your friends.

Healthy friendships require the following:

- positivity
- consistency
- vulnerability
- conversation
- energy

Setting boundaries with those who have already crossed or broken them can be challenging, and you may encounter resistance. If so, be completely honest and reaffirm the barrier once more. Then, if necessary for your wellbeing, you may need to distance yourself by, for example, adjusting your activities or not returning their calls.

Family

Setting limits with family members may be quite challenging as a history of intimate personal connection, affection, and emotion are frequently present.

Here's how to establish boundaries with a relative:

- Recognize that your requirements are just as crucial as theirs.
- Make sure they understand how important this is to you.
- Strike a balance between being firm and being nice.
- Be prepared to leave if they persistently transgress your limits.

Intimate Relationships

Many of the suggestions above also apply to marriage and other close relationships. Your relationship will thrive when you and your partner can openly discuss your needs and wants.

When we learn to place limits on our relationships, we also learn to recognize which connections are beneficial and which ones are not. If people we care about ignore, challenge, or cut us off when we set boundaries, that's a sign that the relationship is unhealthy and has to end.

Healthy relationships are the result of healthy limits. To create a good and long-lasting connection, set the following five types of boundaries:

- physical: no injury or violence
- emotional: freedom of expression, including when and how to express disappointments
- sexual: what you are and are not comfortable with
- intellectual: subjects you won't address
- financial: how you'll divide money and decide what to buy

Establishing Yours

Are you having trouble establishing boundaries in your relationships? Here are some practical suggestions to help you get started.

Begin Small

The easiest approach to getting comfortable with setting limits if you've never done it before is to begin with something minor. Before defining sexual limits, for example, you might want to specify physical ones for kissing and embracing. When starting a new job, be clear about the kind of hours your life permits you to work. Don't be afraid to specify that your schedule needs to be honored and respected.

Start Early

It's usually preferable to establish boundaries early on in a relationship, whether romantic or not, rather than trying to enforce them afterward.

Start With Some Introspection

When establishing limits, it's helpful first to consider the context in which you'll be putting them into effect.

Write down thoughts that come to mind using a pen and paper. Then consider:

- when you felt secure
- moments when you have felt uneasy
- what caused these emotions
- people you know that you think would handle this situation effectively (or previous methods you've used to cope with this issue).

How Does It Make You Feel?

Once you've chosen a personal limit, give yourself time to consider how it makes you feel. Do you feel more secure or satisfied knowing what your limitations are? Do you worry that the limit may be too flexible or too strict?

Recognize the Benefits

Boundaries should promote individual empowerment. It might be a little awkward to set limits, but remember how the barrier you just established will make your life better.

Develop Your Communication Skills

Establishing limits is one thing—it's another to communicate them to others. If you don't communicate your boundaries to others, they won't know what they are.

Here is a quick foundation for effectively communicating your boundaries:

- Point out the issue or prospective issue.
- Give a concrete example of how you would rather see people behave.
- Share your thoughts about what this signifies and why you've decided to put up this barrier.

Put Consistency Into Practice

Enforcing your limits is a crucial part of expressing them. It entails having the self-assurance to set boundaries and discuss them openly with the people in your life. If you do, your limits may stay manageable. Being consistent, however, might put you at risk of encountering people who push your personal boundaries in the future. If, and when, this happens, gently remind them of why you created the boundary in the first place. Stand your ground firmly.

Final Thoughts

Setting boundaries is essential for your mental health and welfare, even though someone who isn't used to doing so may first feel guilty or selfish. Although appropriate boundaries can take various forms depending on the situation, it's crucial to establish them in every aspect of our lives where we interact with people.

Finally, while having boundaries is vital, respecting those of others, including our partners, supervisors, coworkers, parents, and everyone else we come into contact with, is also essential.

Chapter 6:

Thanking Your Stars

Those who frequently engage in the practice of gratitude—that is, those who pause to consider the many blessings in their lives—report feeling happier, more energized, more at peace, more generous, and healthier overall.

One would assume that only one of these conclusions would be strong enough to persuade you to take action. If you're anything like me, though, this drive only lasts for about three days before choosing to watch stand-up comedians on Netflix instead of writing in my gratitude journal every night.

So what does it mean to be thankful, and how can it help you overcome your anxiety?

What Is Gratitude?

The Latin term *gratia*, which signifies grace, graciousness, or gratitude, is where we get our modern English word "gratitude" (Harvard Health Publishing, 2021). Gratitude embraces all these meanings. The emotion of gratitude is one of appreciation for a person's good fortune, whether material or immaterial. Many people assume that something or someone other than themselves is responsible for their good fortune. In reality, we can manifest our own good fortune within our own selves by practicing gratitude regularly. Being grateful for your human, natural, and divine blessings strengthens relationships with those blessings and the world around them.

According to positive psychology studies, feeling grateful increases happiness. Practicing gratitude has been shown to positively affect a person's well-being, health, and resilience in the face of adversity, as well as improve the quality of their interpersonal connections.

It can be expressed in many ways, and you can use it to change your present and future perspectives. Not certain what you have to feel thankful for right now? How about the little things, like a pretty flower, rain, or simply being alive? Luckily you can cultivate gratitude through practice, regardless of how grateful you presently are.

Gratitude: The Science

Gratitude gives us the means to embrace all that contributes to the uniqueness of our life. It is more than simply a pleasant emotion for the positive developments in your life; it also includes the openness to shift your focus to take in more of the blessings surrounding you.

One of the foremost authorities on the science of thankfulness, Robert Emmons, a psychology professor at the University of California, Davis, describes gratitude as having two components (*How to Practice Gratitude*, 2019). First, individuals can become aware of the blessings and positive things in their surroundings. The second component is acknowledging that you do not create your good fortune but instead benefit from the kindness of others. In other words, appreciation makes people aware that they couldn't have achieved their goals without the support of others.

A Gratitude-Based Mindset

Gratitude is a more profound emotion rather than a fleeting sensation of joy. Researchers that have examined written thankfulness therapies, such as gratitude diaries or letters, have discovered advantages for a person's mental health and well-being. According to peer-reviewed studies, gratitude practices not only make you feel happier with life, they even increase your self-esteem (*How to Practice Gratitude*, 2019).

The Science: Become More Content

Over 300 persons receiving therapy participated in one university study. One randomized group composed a letter of thankfulness once a week for three weeks, while the others did not.. At the follow-up 12 weeks following this writing activity, the thankfulness group reported noticeably better mental health when compared to the others.

The habit of listing blessings is another way to express appreciation in writing. Researchers discovered that participants who kept a daily gratitude journal in which they recorded three positive events from the previous day and considered their significance, as well as the factors that contributed to those events, were considerably happier and less sad six months after the trial had concluded (*How to Practice Gratitude*, 2019).

How It Works: It Increases Positive Recall

Precisely how do these techniques help to enhance our mental health?

Often, people are more aware of their disadvantages than the advantages they encounter. They tend to think more about the negative side of things, which in turn starts to reflect in their reality and daily life. Thankfully, the same is true on the flip side. Studies have revealed that we may heighten sensations of joy and optimism by focusing more on the positive side of things. This helps to shape our reality into a more vibrant, uplifting one.

The more we think about something, the more real it becomes to us. Seeing the beautiful things around you becomes simpler by strengthening your positive memory bias in difficult situations.

Why Do It: To Strengthen Resilience

It is not simply about being happy and cheerful; lasting gratitude doesn't call for you to push away or suppress unpleasant feelings. Instead, practice enhances happy emotions more than it mitigates negative emotions. Gratitude enhances your ability to view the bigger picture and makes you more resilient when faced with challenges.

The Neuroscientific Study of Gratitude

In one of her writings, Emily Fletcher, the creator of Ziva, a well-known website for meditation instruction, described gratitude as a "natural antidepressant." When appreciation is practiced consistently, the benefits can be similar to those of drugs. The physiological foundation for it is at the neurotransmitter level, resulting in a sensation of prolonged enjoyment and contentment (Ackerman, 2017).

Dopamine and serotonin, two essential neurotransmitters involved in emotion, are released when we express and receive appreciation. These give us a positive feeling and instantly lift our spirits, bringing along an inner sense of joy.

Through practice, we can encourage the development of these positive brain connections and, eventually, cultivate an eternally thankful and optimistic personality by expressing gratitude daily.

The Effects of Gratitude

Gratitude profoundly affects bodily processes and psychological conditions like stress, anxiety, and depression (Ackerman, 2017). It also improves self-love and empathy.

Gratitude Dispels Negative Feelings

The area of the brain that controls all emotional experiences is known as the limbic system. This structure comprises the thalamus, hypothalamus, amygdala, hippocampus, and cingulate gyrus. Studies have demonstrated that appreciation causes the hippocampus and amygdala, the two key regions controlling emotions, memory, and body function, to become active and improve.

Gratitude Lessens Suffering

According to *Counting Blessings vs. Burdens* (Emmons & McCullough, 2003), a research on the impact of thankfulness on physical health, 16% of patients who kept gratitude journals reported fewer pain symptoms (Ackerman, 2017). They were more eager to exercise and comply with the therapeutic process.

A further look into the issue revealed that thankfulness gives us more energy and lowers our subjective perception of pain by controlling our dopamine levels.

Gratitude Enhances the Quality of Sleep

Receiving and performing little acts of kindness activates the hypothalamus, which governs all bodily functions, including sleep.

It induces hypothalamic regulation, which naturally promotes deeper, better sleep every night. It has been scientifically proven that a grateful and compassionate mind is more likely to sleep soundly and awaken each morning feeling renewed and energized (Zahn et al., 2009).

Gratitude Helps to Manage Stress

In one of their studies on gratitude and appreciation, McCraty and Childre (2004) discovered that individuals who felt appreciative had a substantial drop in cortisol, the stress hormone. They were more immune to emotional setbacks and bad experiences, and their heart function improved.

Numerous credible research studies have confirmed that cultivating thankfulness makes us more resilient to stress. Seeing and appreciating the simple things in life might rewire our brains so we can approach the current situation with more awareness and a broader perspective.

It Lessens Anxiety

Gratitude significantly lessens the signs of despair and anxiety by lowering the stress hormones and controlling autonomic nervous system functioning. An increase in the neuronal modulation of our prefrontal cortex, which is the part of the brain in charge of controlling negative emotions like guilt, shame, and aggression, is connected at the neurochemical level with feelings of appreciation.

Because of this, those who express their thanks aloud or in writing tend to be more sympathetic and optimistic.

How Does It Alleviate Anxiety?

According to research, feeling grateful has a calming effect, in addition to its positive impacts on relationships, mental health, and stress reduction. Numerous studies have found that using thankfulness treatments to combat anxiety is a free, easy, and effective strategy (Khorrami, 2020). Being grateful encourages self-awareness and decreases harmful self-talk.

Gratitude is particularly beneficial in two ways:

You learn to understand yourself better. Stress might result from our excessive self-criticism. To counter this, we can aspire to behave in a more self-compassionate, self-understanding, and easygoing manner. Gratitude is associated with a less judgmental, less punitive, and more sympathetic connection with the self.

Being thankful makes people more likely to be kind, understanding, supportive, and compassionate toward themself and others when difficulties and disappointments arise. As you've probably gathered by now, practicing self-awareness and relaxation may very well be connected to our sense of gratitude.

It dispels negative self-talk. Also known as repetitive negative thinking (RNT), negative self-talk is common in situations where people are experiencing stress, irritation, or continuous concern, all of which can lead to escalating anxiety levels.

One positive finding from a 2019 German study is that appreciation may help curb negative thoughts (Khorrami, 2020). Researchers found that a six-week app-based appreciation intervention significantly reduced RNT. Interestingly, RNT was connected to a higher risk of Alzheimer's Disease development in a 2020 study on Alzheimer's and dementia. The study also found that gratitude may lower Alzheimer's disease incidence by defending against RNT.

Developing Gratitude

Simply thanking someone is inadequate. Although it may provide immediate satisfaction, being truly grateful must develop into a habit to rewire your brain. You may adopt certain behaviors to make appreciation a consistent aspect of your character.

Here are some ways in which you can develop gratitude:

Keep a Diary

Keep a thankfulness diary and list three things you are grateful for each morning or evening.

In writing down the good things that have happened to you, you will come to appreciate the beauty of life and rediscover the treasure trove of happy memories you had buried deep within your mind.

Take Time to Reflect

Experts recommend meditation as a method of handling practically everything. It's quite beneficial for cultivating thankfulness, too. Look for a quiet place to sit and close your eyes. Concentrate on some simple positive things in your everyday life and give thanks for them. Then take a few moments to ponder on how far you have come in your life and the people who have helped you along the way. Give thanks for that journey. Now, think of the positive effects *you* have had in other people's lives as well, then give thanks for being a part of those experiences, too. After this reflection, you will soon find yourself in a much more peaceful state of mind.

Speak With Loved Ones

Express your gratitude for their presence in your life!

Although it may sound foolish, doing this is a great method to develop thankfulness. Call every one of your loved ones and express your gratitude for having them in your life. Tell them how their presence has improved and enriched certain aspects of your existence. You'll begin to appreciate and realize how fortunate you are to have family and friends, and you'll learn to value them more than ever.

Gratitude in Nature

I appreciate the lessons in compassion that nature has given me. The natural world teaches us a lot about how to build a life focused on connections, abundance, and generosity. I'd like to offer three teachings about nature's gracious design that are very important to me in the spirit of giving thanks and sharing.

1. Nature begins with a good deed and calls for an equally generous reaction. Let's take sunlight, the source of energy for all life on Earth. Photosynthesis is necessary to transform solar energy into the vital nutrients that the natural world, including humans, needs to survive. There is always enough sunshine to go around, but in order to benefit from it, we must be prepared to actively engage in the compassionate reaction of photosynthesis.

As the sun is constantly giving, generosity is something we also encounter in both our private and professional life. However, we must be willing to accept these acts of kindness and respond to them appreciatively in order to receive them completely.

2. In nature, there are many examples of reciprocal connections based on both need and abundance. We diversify and grow more complex as our natural systems change. Plant-animal interactions work cohesively together to ensure their prosperity and each other's survival. Our joint efforts with the natural world allow us to benefit from an abundant supply of nourishments that would otherwise be unavailable to us. When one species has an excess of a certain nutrient, it may offer that nutrient to another, and so forming a mutually supportive connection.

   By giving our talents and asking for what we need in return, individuals may establish reciprocal connections throughout their lives, too. If we isolate ourselves from other people, we won't be able to make use of the wealth of opportunities and resources that are accessible to us.

3. Nature is designed as an interconnected and supporting system. Nothing in nature exists for itself, and the following beautifully capture just that:

   - Rivers do not consume their own water.
   - Trees do not consume their own fruit.
   - The sun does not shine for itself.
   - The scent of a flower does not exist for itself.

Nature's law is that we should all live for one another. What if we led our lives in accordance with this affirmation of our inherent interdependence? It could alter our natural tendency toward self-interest. If we keep in mind that nature is made to sustain and nurture all of its elements, it can assist us in being less afraid of our own shortcomings.

We may choose how we want to lead our life. We have the option of living in constant terror and clutching our possessions until we pass away, or we can choose to live a love-centered life in which we generously share our time and resources with others and the natural world in order to feel safe and secure (Dr. Kathleen Allen, 2019).

Gratitude Exercises

We can express thankfulness to others, ourselves, a higher power, or even "the universe" in limitless ways. Here are some of the most popular and effective appreciation exercises and activities.

The Jar

The appreciation jar is a simple yet powerful activity.

- Find a jar and customize it with a ribbon or stickers. Be as creative as you want in giving your jar personality.
- Place a note of gratitude inside your jar daily.

Over time, you will fill a jar with many reasons to be grateful and enjoy life. Take a few notes from the jar to cheer yourself up when you're feeling down.

The Rock

This one may seem ridiculous. A rock? Can a rock teach you gratitude? This technique works because the rock is a tangible reminder of what you are grateful for.

- First, find a rock you like!
- Keep this rock in your pocket, on your desk, or on a chain around your neck or wrist.
- Pause to appreciate it whenever you see or touch it. Think of one thing that makes you happy, such as the sun beaming on you at that moment, or a smile from a stranger. After taking the stone out of your pocket or off your body at night, think of everything that you were grateful for that day.

This will help you recall your blessings and give you a mini-mindfulness moment. It will help you focus and get out of your head, while also encouraging optimistic thinking.

The Flower

What on earth is a gratitude flower? Let me show you.

- Cut out a colorful paper circle, and write "Things I'm thankful for" or "My Family" inside. Cut out flower petals in as many colors as you like.
- Write notes of appreciation on each petal, then glue or tape these to the center to create your flower.

So simple, yet so powerful, this gratitude flower will help remind you of all the beauty and abundance in your life.

The Box

This gratitude box is a meaningful way to express your thanks and connect with loved ones.

- Make or purchase a box—the nicer, the better!—and fill it with appreciation notes for your loved one.
- Gather words or more letters about this person from others to fill the box with even more love and gratitude. Put the message(s) in the box, wrap or tie a bow around it, and present it to your loved one as a gift.

They will feel so loved!

Prompts

Here are some gratitude prompts to help you start, maintain, or restart your gratitude practice. Simply fill in the blanks!

Start with the phrase "I appreciate three…"

- smells
- touchable things
- tastes
- animals
- people

Take a Walk

A stroll may clear your thoughts during a difficult period. Walking with a thankfulness focus can reduce stress and improve well-being, much like meditation.

It increases stress-reducing endorphins, heart health, and blood circulation while lowering lethargy and blood pressure. While taking this walk, observe your surroundings. Observe nature's colors, sounds, and smells. If you're walking barefoot, feel the ground under your feet.

Gratitude walks with friends or partners are even more powerful, as you may express your gratitude for walking and appreciating each moment together.

Reflection

Meditation and self-awareness require reflection. Gratitude is all about self-reflecting on what you are blessed enough to have.

Follow these steps for valuable reflection:

- Relax. Breathe deeply to calm down.
- Focus on your surroundings—smell, taste, touch, sight, sound. Say "Thank you."
- Consider your friends, family, and relationships. Say "Thank you" to yourself.
- Focus on yourself: you are unique, gifted with ideas, communication, learning from the past and planning for the future, and overcoming hardship. Say "Thank you."

Finally, appreciate life's little gifts. You were born into great prosperity and have the opportunity to grow through precious health, culture, and spiritual lessons.

The Letter/Email/Visit

Writing a thank-you note to someone special may be the most effective feel-good activity. Expressing your emotions and sharing them with amazing individuals cultivates appreciation and happiness. If you're not sure what to write, think about a nice deed you still need to thank a friend, relative, coworker, instructor, or mentor for.

- Be specific in your letter and explain how this individual has affected your life. Describe how often you recall their compassion or charity and how this makes you feel.
- Re-read your letter to make sure it is clear and conveys the desired message. Pay particular attention to spelling and grammar!
- Fold it nicely and deliver this letter by hand, if possible.
- Make it a surprise!

Meditate

Meditation can be challenging, especially when the mind wanders and distracts you. Still, if you practice it regularly, you will experience immense thankfulness and delight.

During a gratitude meditation, instead of focusing on your breath, simply think about everything you're grateful for.

Spiritual Gratitude

As a spiritual practice, gratitude has been described as a mental attitude and a behavioral pattern. However, we can choose to see it as a language or a framework within which we may build and make meaning of our lives (Brussat & Brussat, 2022). These linguistic guidelines apply to every area of life. Its structure shows a network of connections between us and Divinity and between us and just about every other aspect of creation.

To understand the grammatical rules of gratitude, try to say "thank you" for both good and bad things, for individuals, animals, belongings, art, memories, and dreams. Think about all that you have and thank your Creator, God, Heaven, or any Higher power you believe in. Affirm blessings over everyone and everything you come into contact with, and show gratitude for their presence in your life. By helping others, we help ourselves.

To practice spiritual gratitude, you must vow to have at least one daily cue that reminds you to be grateful.

Examples from my own life include:

- My reminder to be grateful comes whenever I reach for a fork to start eating. I say a prayer and offer thanks to the Divine for the blessing of another meal.

- Whenever I leave my car, I am thankful that I have arrived safely at my destination.
- When I go through the entrance of my house, I am immediately brought back to the present and reminded to be grateful for everything that I have. I say thanks for having a home, a warm bed at night, a hot shower after a long day, and for leaving to go to the job I am lucky enough to have.

Find a cue that works for you, and remember to give thanks to the Divine Creator, who blesses us day in and day out.

Maintaining Gratitude

Overall, gratitude can help people feel less anxious in interesting and notable ways. Thankfulness therapies are recommended by researchers based on the results of several studies, though other researchers warn against using gratitude as the *only* strategy to reduce anxiety. Still, the overwhelming body of research indicates much to gain from thankfulness, including support in the battle against worry.

Here are some strategies for establishing and maintaining gratitude:

Refresh Your Gratitude

Writing in a gratitude notebook is effective because it gradually alters our perception of events by refocusing our attention. Even if you may always be happy for your wonderful family, writing "I'm grateful for my family" every week won't keep your mind searching for new reasons to be thankful. Your thankfulness practice can be significantly improved by widening your perspective on the world. Make a game of discovering something new every day.

Realize the Benefits of Your Gratitude Practice

Being enthusiastic about the advantages of thankfulness is fantastic because it provides us with the push we need to change. But we are only human, and unplanned events might cause us to stumble and lose momentum. By keeping in mind both the potential rewards of forming a new

79

habit and the challenges it may provide, we are more motivated to put in the work necessary to achieve our goals. Recognize potential challenges and make plans to overcome them.

Mix It Up

Autonomy, or the freedom to do things how we like, is one of the main factors that spark the innate drive to see a task through to completion. So don't restrict yourself—if journaling is getting old, try out fresh and imaginative ways to keep track of your grateful moments.

Be Loud About It

The main factor influencing our happiness is our relationships with others, so it seems sensible to keep others in mind while we increase our thankfulness. We increase our advantages by directing our appreciation toward the people we love rather than the things or circumstances for which we are grateful.

Why not actively include people in your show of thankfulness while doing it? For example, dinnertime is a great time to reflect on the day's blessings and express gratitude to one another!

Final Thoughts: Using Gratitude to Combat Anxiety

Practicing thankfulness is not usually suggested as a way to calm anxiety. It is surprisingly underappreciated.

Still, I have found that it has brought me remarkable benefits. Realizing that there are positive aspects of your life might help you, too, to put your anxieties and concerns in perspective and understand that they are not as important as all the positive aspects. This realization reduces worry and frees you to take action on the tasks you have been putting off.

What are you grateful for today?

Chapter 7:

Shoo, Negativity!

When starting a new project, every person has different and diverse ideas, attitudes, and behaviors. All these variations are influenced by our own perspectives, personal convictions, and presumptions toward the situation.

When you are anxious, your negative emotions and cognitive patterns dominate your positive ones. Sometimes expressing gratitude is not enough, and fear and feelings of unworthiness may start to rule your decisions. Working to alter your thinking and feelings toward a particular situation is what Cognitive Behavioral Therapy (CBT) aims to achieve.

What Is Cognitive Behavioral Therapy?

CBT is a treatment that focuses on identifying and restructuring harmful thinking, patterns, and behaviors. That is to say, CBT can aid in developing new habits of thought and action.

For instance, you could be feeling the following when starting a new job:

- **Anxious:** You could be experiencing anxiety since this is a new setting with unfamiliar coworkers and procedures. You may feel like you'll never be able to adjust—you may even consider calling in sick on your first day.
- **Neutral:** Because you've previously held various jobs, you could be experiencing no emotion. Work is, after all, work. You might think, *I'm going out to supper as soon as the day is through.*
- **Excited:** You could experience excitement when beginning a new professional journey and taking on brand-new tasks. You may think, *I can't wait to work on that new project!*

Your attitude towards a new challenge all depends on you, and on how you choose to look at life.

Cognitive Behavioral Therapy in Treating Anxiety

Much of our experience is based on perception. By eliminating negative ideas, we make room for more constructive ones, thereby improving our experience and making any unpleasant feelings we feel more manageable.

Over time, your behavior toward a scenario might alter if you have unfavorable views. Think about a child who gets bullied and consistently feels terrible about going to school; they could start making up reasons not to attend.

These actions begin to repeat themselves over time and start to slowly form patterns. By using CBT, you can learn to recognize these patterns and take steps to modify them and the associated emotions you experience. With enough time, it may be possible to stop these actions from occurring again.

CBT can assist you in recognizing the interconnected ideas, feelings, activities, and bodily sensations that contribute to increased anxiety and depression. By realizing your thought patterns and stopping your mind from getting carried away, you open yourself up to a world of greater possibilities. You no longer feel like you have to avoid potentially stressful circumstances.

Accepting the Dinner Invitation

Let's take the situation of having low self-esteem as an example. Perhaps you attempt to avoid social gatherings because being around many people makes you anxious.

When you receive an invitation to a group event at a restaurant, you anticipate a big attendance. Your first impression is, *No way. I'll have to start a conversation. What if others think I'm awkward?*

You could experience anxiety or perhaps a slight panic. You abruptly inform the host that you're not feeling well and can't make it to their event.

While this habit can temporarily improve your mood, it only serves to make you more anxious in social situations. The issue is that this negative cycle of ideas, feelings, and actions is continued when you consistently avoid the circumstances that make you feel anxious or afraid.

Instead, try the following:

- Start learning some relaxation techniques you may apply the next time you receive a social invitation.
- Whenever worry starts to set in, take note of the first things that come to mind.
- Try to replace negative ideas and emotions with more sensible ones. This method of cognitive restructuring is also called reframing.

As you implement these practices, you will notice that you become more able to act against the fear and thus better adept at handling situations that once caused you worry and anxiety.

Cognitive Distortions

Cognitive distortions are flawed thinking patterns ingrained in us. Everybody experiences them, but those who deal with sadness and anxiety tend to experience them more frequently than others.

We often believe that anxiety or despair are brought on by unfavorable circumstances, generally events beyond our control. However, the narrative we tell ourselves about the occurrence is frequently the *most* important factor contributing to our negative feelings or the escalation of an already challenging circumstance (Star, 2022).

Here are some illustrations of distorted thinking:

Catastrophizing

A particularly skewed thought pattern that significantly increases anxiety is called catastrophizing. It occurs when we assume the worst, predict disaster, or perceive something as much worse than it truly is. Sounds recognizable? Imagining the worst possible outcome immediately is one of my superpowers!

When we consider the obstacles or situations we confront, we instantly imagine the worst-case scenario. This is carried out in our brains as we play what-if. When this happens, we keep asking ourselves, *What if this worst-case situation occurs?*

Catastrophizing often comes in two different types. First, a contemporary event is given an unfavorable "spin, for example, *driving on icy roads is dangerous and unpredictable.* The second kind happens when we try to predict the future and worry about everything that may go wrong. *Oh no! My family is driving up this weekend and the roads will likely be iced over. What if they lose control of their car and swerve off the road? They are not going to make it!*

While breaking the cycle might be challenging, you can take several straightforward measures to recognize this situation and prevent the cycle from continuing before it spirals out of control with worry. Try this instead:

- Take note of the events around the times you catastrophize.
- Start keeping a journal of your negative ideas. With as much objectivity as you can, describe what occurred and your thoughts on the matter. Then describe your actions or reactions.
- Make a mental shift to be more tolerant and hopeful.
- Realize that the worst scenario that "might" occur isn't necessarily all that bad.

Jumping to Conclusions

According to cognitive therapy theories, we are what we believe ourselves to be. Many people have a problem with making hasty judgments. In fact, jumping to conclusions based on insufficient information is irresponsible.

Jumping to conclusions means making unfavorable judgments based on scant or nonexistent facts, and may be harmful in a variety of ways. Assumptions tend to be emotional rather than reason-based, and could lead to the other person (or yourself!) feeling threatened or attacked. Arguments and longer-term issues may result if you frequently draw wrong inferences about others, which could easily lead to relationship difficulties.

It can also heighten emotions of anxiousness and impair how you view yourself. This is like a vicious cycle—people who feel anxiety and depression often make snap judgments that worsen their symptoms.

Nervous people, for instance, become considerably more anxious when they believe that others are criticizing them. Individuals with depression may experience worsening signs of melancholy and hopelessness if they leap to conclusions and believe nothing will ever improve.

Preventing Hasty Judgments

Although the cognitive bias of leaping to conclusions is quite prevalent, you can take steps to reduce how frequently you think in this way. The following actions might be helpful:

- **Verify the details:** Before making a judgment or choice, start by learning as much as possible. Focus on the facts.
- **Confront your thoughts:** If you catch yourself drawing swift judgments, challenge them. *Are these accusations actually true? Why do I think they are true? Do I have proof?*
- **Pose inquiries:** Try asking before drawing conclusions about someone else's thinking. Many misunderstandings may be resolved by expressing your concerns and receiving a clear response. Open communication is key.
- **Take a different view:** Consider the circumstance from an outsider's perspective. What might they make of the circumstance? What details would they require to draw a reliable conclusion?

Getting all the information, questioning your beliefs, asking questions, and changing your perspective may help you think more clearly and avoid hasty decisions.

Personalization

This occurs when you hold yourself accountable for circumstances that are genuinely beyond your control. People who struggle with personalization could experience guilt or humiliation for being powerless over uncontrollable circumstances. Making an irrelevant event or circumstance about yourself is another example of personalizing.

Personalization leads to emotional discomfort. You feel uneasy, anxious, or suffer from impostor syndrome, and you keep expecting others to see that *you* are the issue or the one at fault.

This may also resemble the famous three *no-nos*: ought, must, and should, which are to be avoided at all costs! People dealing with anxiety, despair, guilt, shame, poor self-esteem, low self-worth, or self-criticism frequently think this way. *I must force myself to go out and socialize. I should have known better!*

Inversely, you may find yourself in the pattern of pointing the finger at other people, or maybe even at yourself under particular circumstances. For instance, you might blame yourself and accept responsibility for something that was out of your control. Similarly, you might blame other people for something of your own wrongdoing.

Assigning blame to others for your problems absolves you of accountability, though taking responsibility for your actions is vital to your healing journey. We can often observe this practice of passing the blame in romantic partnerships. Let's take the subject of family debt as an example. Despite your own contribution to the situation, you might blame your husband for it entirely. Placing the blame on your spouse takes the burden of dealing with financial challenges off your shoulders. "It's not my fault we're in debt. If my partner was better at managing our finances, this never would have occurred," you might say.

How to Get Out and Avoid Personalization

Personalizing thoughts can lose their power quite quickly by practicing a simple exercise called ICE. It can assist to bring your dark thought patterns up to the surface, dissolve them, and help you develop more mental strength against them.

Next time you find yourself in an emotionally uncomfortable situation, refer to the following:

- **I: Identify** your personalizing thoughts.
- **C: Call** it what it is: a cognitive distortion.
- **E: Examine** the idea to see if it is reasonable. Are you actually to blame for their joy, disappointment, or difficulties? Similarly, recognize your lack of responsibility if it exists. Acknowledge if you are assigning blame when, in fact, you should be taking responsibility for something.

Separate your worth from the accomplishments or failings of others. You are not responsible for their actions. Make an effort to stop blaming yourself instantly, and consider if doing so makes sense. Bring in some gray areas to your thoughts instead of seeing situations as strictly black or white. Try to look at events from the outside and consider all potential causes.

Mental Filtering

This seems like one of those "cup-half-empty" situations that pop up frequently. You don't perceive a person or circumstance for all the positive aspects; instead, you notice only the drawbacks or shortcomings. Mental filtering focuses on these specifics while ignoring or refusing to accept contrary facts.

This type of filtering draws greater focus to your displeasure, can amplify particular circumstances, and results in unpleasant experiences.

In addition, it may cause a distortion of the scenario, resulting in increased levels of worry, panic, and despair. This is because it may filter out the good aspects of the circumstance that may assist in overcoming the negative ones. This vicious cycle is often made worse by self-defeating thoughts, which rise along with nervousness, uncertainty, and distress.

Overcoming Mental Filters and Finding a Way Out

Until you realize that you are applying this cognitive distortion, it might be challenging to stop engaging in mental filters. Once again, do your best to apply the ICE approach.

I - Identify Your Emotions

Become aware of your cognitive processes. Checking in with yourself might be useful in learning how to spot a mental filter. For instance, if you catch yourself whining, consider why. Or, if you're feeling down or nervous, try to figure out why you're feeling that way. Be aware if you are obsessing over something that has already occurred or that you may reasonably (or unreasonably!) expect to occur.

C - Call It What It Is

Determine whatever emotions you are experiencing. How exactly are you feeling? When you dwell on a bad experience, do you notice that your anxiety or depression worsens?

E - Explore a Different Scenario

Do you sometimes use mental filtration, and other times you don't? If you catch yourself engaging in mental filters—or any kind of cognitive distortion—, ask yourself why you could be doing it. Do you tend to apply mental filters only on Sundays, for instance? Do you engage in this behavior while speaking with particular individuals? Do you solely use this when performing specific tasks? Once more, it could be very revealing to learn why you employ mental filtering in a particular way.

Take this exercise one step further. Would other people reach the same conclusions if you presented them with this filter? Or would they raise an eyebrow and give you that dumbfounded or inquisitive "Do you truly believe this?" look?

Writing down your filtered thinking and other interpretations may prove useful, especially at first, while you figure out how to push your mental boundaries and end your cycle of defeat.

Overgeneralization

To overgeneralize is to attribute one experience, or a small range of experiences, to all our experiences. This can be attributed to past, present, or future affairs.

For example, "I failed to submit a project at work. I'm a bad employee and am often forgetful. Next week, I'll also have trouble remembering to turn in my work."

Overgeneralization may be harmful in its most severe forms and can cause prejudices such as discrimination, sexism, and homophobia. People with these prejudices base a whole group of people on their own constrained experiences. After seeing a woman drive poorly, for instance, they may believe that all women drive poorly.

In some respects, overgeneralizing is very black or white, much like the all-or-nothing mindset. Both kinds of cognitive distortions have little, if any, margin for error, and are characterized by phrases like "always," "never," and "every." Additionally, both thought patterns have been linked to low self-esteem, anxiety, sadness, and perfectionism. They frequently reinforce or intensify negative beliefs about yourself, others, and life in general. This kind of thinking can easily damage your connections with others by increasing your feelings of resentment against them and building a sense of judgment and condemnation.

How to Avoid Generalizing Too Much

Here are some methods you can use to stop yourself from overgeneralizing situations. Have some faith in the process!

Determine Thought Patterns

This may sound redundant, but becoming aware of your thought patterns is key, and almost always the first step to fixing any problem. You won't be able to alter anything until you pinpoint exactly what it is that needs to be altered. Pay attention to your thoughts and note any ideas you have. You can use a thinking diary to jot down anything that doesn't feel right. In this way, you might be able to spot trends as you write down your ideas and become more conscious of them.

Be as Truthful as Possible

You may find yourself thinking, *I forgot to take the trash out again! I frequently fail to remember important things.* Instead, try replacing this with, *I forgot to take out the trash this morning. I need to pay more attention to my surroundings.*

Keep in Mind That You Are Human

You're a human, therefore you will make errors. There is no avoiding that. However, shaming yourself for errors or overgeneralizing will only worsen your feelings. Treating yourself as though you are incapable of making errors is unfair to yourself.

Work on Cultivating a Growth Mindset

Embodying a growth mindset means:
- being able to adapt and think outside the box
- believing in your capacity to change, develop, and learn

- accepting challenges
- welcoming criticism
- believing that failure is an opportunity to learn
- feeling inspired by others' achievements

Black and White Thinking

When you think in all-or-nothing terms, your opinions are split into opposite extremes. Everything is categorized as either black or white, including your self-perception and life events. There isn't much, if any, gray space left after this.

Absolute phrases like "never" or "ever" are frequently used in all-or-nothing thinking. The failure to identify options or solutions in a situation is another example of this kind of flawed thinking. If someone has anxiety or depression, this often results in them only perceiving the negative aspects of any given circumstance. This way of thinking leads people to assume that they are either utterly successful in life or ultimately unsuccessful.

How to Change Unfavorable Thoughts

You'll notice a beneficial difference if you stop:

- concentrating on the negative
- using words with no restrictions, such as "never" or "nothing"

Instead:

- recognize your strengths
- accept that failures are inevitable
- consider the bright side of circumstances

When you're having trouble seeing things from several perspectives, sometimes it helps to talk things over with people you know and trust.

Labeling

This refers to giving yourself a name after a bad incident. For example, you may conclude that *I'm an awkward person* after feeling uncomfortable during a social gathering.

Do not give yourself any labels other than positive characteristics. That incident you had was just a bad experience—it does not mean you are awkward and does not define who you are as a person.

Attribution Errors

Similar to overgeneralizations, it is absurd to think you can accurately predict a person's motivations for their behavior. Their actions may, or may not, have been intended.

As has often been the case in my experience, people tend to act without even realizing it. Their actions may result from an accident, chance or even unexpected repercussions, and it is highly likely that their behaviors aren't or weren't intended for you.

We assess ourselves based on intention, yet judge others based on behavior. When someone's actions have no noticeable reason, it might be challenging for us to identify the source.

Keep the following in mind:

- Be mindful about common knowledge. Suppose most people generally react the same when placed in a particular scenario, and if that is the case, it can then be assumed that *the scenario* is the explanation for the observed reaction.
- Consider what your behavior would have been in the same circumstance. What would you have done differently?
- Try to identify hidden causes and significantly less obvious ones. Did the other person have a bad day or receive upsetting news before their reaction?

Emotional Reasoning

Simply put, emotional reasoning is the belief that your subjective experience of a situation must be the real way it is. Since you consider your account of events to be true and correct, you tend to reject information

91

that contradicts your impressions. You don't look at the facts. For example, if someone behaved oddly with you when you crossed them on the street, you might presume that they have an issue with you when, in fact, they're simply preoccupied with other things more important to them.

Likewise, it stands to reason that if someone is experiencing feelings of helplessness, it is because the problem at hand is too complex for them. This is also a major component of procrastination—you are more inclined to put off or refuse to start a given task if you believe it is overwhelming.

It's vital to hear someone out and acknowledge their emotional experience, but it's also important to provide intellectual support by presenting all sides of an issue. Emotional reasoning ignores facts and holds the emotional response as "concrete evidence" of the presumption of truth.

Anxiety, despair, and procrastination nearly often include significant emotional reasoning. For instance, you might assume you are in danger if you have anxiety. If you're sad, you may feel like time is running out on you. If you're overburdened, you could decide that the work is too great for you to handle. Emotional reasoning can affect your self-worth, confidence, and self-esteem, even if you know that your sentiments are unsupported by logic.

How to Escape and Get Over Emotional Reasoning

The ICE approach may be applied to overcome this way of thinking as well. Here's how:

- **Identify** and describe the sensations you are feeling and what you are thinking. *I'm feeling overwhelmed. My to-do list is never ending and I can't seem to ever catch up with my demands.*
- **Call it what it is.** Acknowledge that you're engaging in emotional reasoning, or any other form of cognitive distortion.
- **Explore the situation** and ask yourself questions that help break down the root of your current feeling. *Do I always feel like this, or only under specific circumstances? What are those particular circumstances in which I feel this way? What could I do so that I don't keep running into the same problem?* Examine the evidence that supports your idea or emotion as well as any facts that conflict with that evidence.

Take a moment to step back from your emotions and ideas and evaluate the issue objectively. Be self-compassionate while attempting to fill your reasoning with logic and facts. Speak to yourself as though you were a close friend who was having trouble with emotional thinking.

Should Statements

Have you ever thought, *I should already have a job; I can't believe it's taking this long*, or, *Everyone around me seems to have a partner. I should have met someone by now!*

In psychological contexts, "should" statements are often regarded as negative self-talk. They are a particular negative thought pattern that fuels anxiety and terror. This kind of flawed reasoning frequently manifests itself in sentences that include the words "should," "ought to," or "must."

Using this self-defeating language frequently causes people to close up and plunge into a world of loneliness and disillusionment. "Should" ultimately robs us of the freedom to follow our instincts and live without feeling compelled to conform to social expectations.

The idea that we "should" have achieved specific life objectives by a certain age is another pressure from society. Let's take, for instance, the false portrayal that by the age of 25, we should have completed college, made a five-year plan, have a career, met the perfect partner, and started our family. Now, that's a lot of pressure for anyone, especially for someone with anxious tendencies!

It is a perfectionist ideal, and letting others paint an image of what we ought to be doing fuels a lot of self-defeating patterns and behaviors. Our welfare is being crippled one "should" at a time.

Thankfully, there are strategies to remove the word "should" from your life.

- **Be mindful**. As soon as you hear a "should" statement, whether coming from yourself or others, write it down.
- **Recognize your triggers.** Make notes on your location when the idea crosses your mind. Afterward, try to connect the statement to the trigger that led to it.
- **Break these statements down.** *Is this "should" statement even feasible given my particular set of circumstances? Who says I should? Is this really the best option for me? Am I treating myself with the same respect and patience I would give to a friend?*

- **Change them to more positive, realistic, and loving remarks about yourself.** *Whether I do or don't, did or didn't, I am enough. I am growing, learning, and getting better everyday.* Repeat these mantras to remind yourself of your worth. Suddenly, instead of representing failed expectations, our "shoulds" become the basis of endless possibilities.
- **Organize your priorities.** It's better to focus on what you want to do rather than what you should accomplish. What truly reflects your values? What would take you one step further in the right direction? Focus on that.

Stop constantly telling yourself that you should. What you say to yourself and other people matters. You may improve your self-awareness and show yourself and the world that *you* are in command of your life simply by changing the way you talk to yourself and accepting more of who you are.

Disqualifying the Positive

This mental distortion repeatedly feeds irrational ideas into your mind and justifies existing pessimism. You've undoubtedly witnessed this cognitive distortion firsthand if you've attempted to reason someone out of a bad mood or have been in a bad mood yourself.

The following scenarios demonstrate what it looks like to invalidate the positives:

- Attributing your achievements to things like good luck, the simplicity of the work, or the generosity of others.
- Dismissing praises and appreciation as insignificant or meaningless.
- Refusing to accept the good things that are happening and focusing solely on the bad.

The results of these are depriving yourself of happiness and believing that your accomplishments don't count or aren't good enough. This reinforces your negative worldview and self-perceptions, which worsens depression symptoms.

How to Remove Yourself From Discomfort

First, you must understand your reasons behind disqualifying the positives. Does excluding the good provide you with a sense of emotional justification, or reinforce your negative assumptions because perhaps you secretly believe they are or could be true? Do you frequently discount good things because of your sadness or anxiety?

Our thoughts greatly influence how we view ourselves and our sense of belonging. It seems reasonable that you would focus on the negativity that "supports" this if you are having trouble with self-defeating ideas or internal conversation. Focusing on the occurrences that confirm these ideas and, by extension, your feelings makes perfect sense.

Your ideas and feelings influence your behaviors. What behaviors are you likely practicing if you are excluding the positive? Do you spend your time ignoring everything positive and then moping about it as a result of your constant focus on the bad?

How to Stop Excluding the Positives

If you tend to disqualify the positives, here are a few tricks to help you stop doing just that.

Learn to Spot the Signs

Checking in with yourself might help you understand how you eliminate the positives. If you have trouble accepting praise, for instance, this is a sign that you should introspect. Didn't you work hard to deserve that praise? If you find yourself moping, it's a good idea to do an internal check to evaluate what you've been telling yourself. Alternatively, figure out what's bothering you if you're feeling down.

Determine Your Emotions

Do you notice your sadness worsening when you dwell on a bad experience? Is this allowing you "permission" to feel whatever feeling you have been focusing on? Do you have anything to learn from this experience? What might make you feel better?

Examine Your Habits

Do you reject the good things in certain circumstances but not in others? If you catch yourself doing this, ask yourself why you could be doing it. Do you, for instance, exclusively practice this behavior with particular individuals? Do you exclude the positives solely when performing specific tasks? It can be interesting to learn why you sometimes utilize this cognitive distortion.

Cognitive Behavioral Therapy Exercises

The exercises below may be used to practically confront and argue repetitive negative thinking (Selva, 2018b).

Testing Your Thoughts

Now that you know what each cognitive distortion is and how each type presents itself, take a moment to contemplate whenever you feel a distortion arising. Challenge your thoughts with the following questions:

- What is the current circumstance? It's likely that whatever you're thinking about, be it an external event or an internal one (such as a strong feeling, a terrible sensation, a visual, a fantasy, a flashback, or a train of thought like *I need to start planning my future*) has just occurred.
- What exactly am I imagining or thinking?
- Which cognitive distortion am I getting wrapped up in?
- What gives me a reason to believe the idea is real?
- What leads me to believe that the concept is partially or fully false?
- What is another perspective on this same situation?
- What options do I have if the worst *does* happen?
- What is the most favorable scenario?
- What is likely to occur?
- If I continue to think the same thing, what will happen?
- What may occur if I altered my perspective?
- If this was happening to someone else, what would I say to that person?
- What is the best course of action at this moment?

Positive Replacement Thoughts

Positive replacement thoughts through self-affirmations and gentle self-talk will prompt you to note all the automatic negative ideas that come to mind. After this, make a conscious effort to generate good thoughts to replace the negative ones.

People who engage in positive self-talk have a positive internal dialogue with themselves. This technique gives them hope and drive. The first action in transforming our negative self-talk into positive self-talk is by recognizing it! As soon as you realize you have a negative thought, counteract it by replacing it with something more uplifting.

When you deliberately tell yourself positive affirmations, you are teaching your brain to gradually rewire itself to believe these things. All of us are composed of our thoughts and previous experiences, so when you actively express your truth—or the truth you wish to convey—your brain starts to believe it, and you start to embody it.

I've compiled a list of my favorite self-affirmations to help you heal and grow.

Self-Affirmations

Here is a list of choices, but feel free to come up with your own empowering statements. Choose a couple of them and either recite them or write them down as soon as you wake up each day. This will help you start your day well and move in the right direction.

- *I have the courage to face my fears.*
- *I am safe and in control.*
- *I take things one day at a time.*
- *I am becoming the person I want to be every day.*
- *I can handle everything that comes my way.*
- *I am doing the best I can, and that is enough.*
- *I accept who I am.*
- *I have faith that everything will work out.*
- *I am getting closer to reaching my goals every single day.*
- *I breathe in peace; I breathe out worry.*
- *I am loved for who I am.*
- *My mistakes do not define me.*

You can transform yourself into a positive thinker even if you aren't naturally optimistic through small, repeated actions, like affirmations, which help rewire your brain to think more optimistically. Focusing on and paying attention to your inner dialogue and self-talk is crucial to your healing journey!

Final Thoughts on Cognitive Behavioral Therapy

Don't get trapped in the vicious cycle of negative beliefs. Catastrophizing, jumping to conclusions, personalization, mental filtering, overgeneralization, black and white thinking, labeling, emotional reasoning, "should" statements, disqualifying the positive—all or any of these may be a major contributing factor to your pain and battle with anxiety.

The phrase "the power of positive thinking" can occasionally come across as an empty promise. In this situation, however, giving your best efforts toward positive thinking may be just what you need to begin to alter your world in the right direction and start feeling better.

All in all, our mind should be our ally. Being able to become more aware of the cognitive distortions that unknowingly consume us is essential to being able to move past them and build resiliency against them. Learn your tendencies and name them for what they are. The more they are brought up to the surface, the more they lose their power.

Chapter 8:

Face Your Fears

With the support of exposure treatment, people can confront and conquer their fears and anxieties about previously overwhelming obstacles. Psychologists and therapists use it to treat phobias and post-traumatic stress disorder (PTSD), among other problems.

Those who have a specific fear are more likely to stay away from whatever it is they associate with that fear. The theory behind exposure treatment is that by exposing patients to distressing stimuli in a safe setting, they can lessen avoidance and conquer their fears.

In this chapter, I will explain all you need to know about exposure treatment, including the conditions it is used to heal, how it operates, and how beneficial it is.

What Is Exposure Treatment?

Exposure therapy is used to treat several types of anxiety disorders, such as phobias, panic attacks, social anxiety disorder, general anxiety disorder, trauma-related stress disorders, and obsessive-compulsive disorder.

By balancing the connection between fear and avoidance, therapists can use exposure therapy to help patients overcome their worries and anxiety. This works by putting them in contact with frightening stimuli in a safe and secure setting.

An individual with social anxiety disorder would, for instance, avoid big gatherings attended by lots of people. In this case, exposure therapy would aim to make patients feel at ease in these social settings by exposing them to the thing or situation they fear.

Exposure treatment may be beneficial in four main ways:

- **Processing of feelings:** By being directly exposed to your source of anxiety, you can develop more realistic thoughts about a fearful stimulus.
- **Extinction:** By repeatedly exposing yourself to whatever you fear, you can eventually overcome your aversion to it.

- **Habituation:** Over time, being exposed to fearful stimuli repeatedly can help you react less strongly.
- **Self-efficacy:** Exposure therapy demonstrates your strength and capacity to face your fears and control your anxiety.

Positive Aspects of Exposure Therapy

The data is strong and demonstrates that exposure therapy relieves symptoms in many patients. Studies have repeatedly demonstrated positive results (*The Advantages and Disadvantages of Exposure Therap*y, 2022).

Exposure therapy is effective for many ailments, including phobias, anxiety disorders, and post-traumatic stress disorder. And because many of these conditions often coexist, exposure therapy may help treat more than one at a time.

Not only does it bring hope for people who have been severely affected by trauma, but patients also learn valuable coping skills like deep breathing as part of the exposure therapy process.

Although it may seem challenging, you could also perform exposure therapy on your own with the help of resources like this book or an online community. It is preferable, however, to be accompanied by a professional for smoother, more holistic results.

Adverse Effects of Exposure Therapy

This form of therapy is relatively long-term and does not take place all at once. It takes more time to obtain specific results than trauma-focused therapies, such as eye movement desensitization and reprocessing.

Exposure therapy is straightforward in principle but challenging to put into practice. As you know, it can be extremely difficult to talk about upsetting or traumatic experiences and tackle these issues head-on. Still, this is a must for exposure therapy, which calls for engaging in physical activity like social interaction. Thinking about doing something versus *really doing that thing* are very different.

Here are additional drawbacks to exposure therapy:

- **It's not very intensive:** People with severe symptoms might not find exposure therapy sufficiently intense for their needs.

- **It's not a one-size-fits-all strategy:** Sadly, not everyone will benefit from exposure therapy. The intricacies underlying anxiety means that some approaches may work more effectively on some than others.
- **Short-term suffering:** Therapy involves working through past traumas, which may worsen short-term stressors.

Types of Exposure Therapy

Exposure therapy comes in many possible forms.

- **Exposure in vivo:** This entails confronting your fear in the actual world. Arachnophobes, for instance, would have to come into contact with spiders.
- **Exposure in mind:** An object or circumstance is vividly imagined. For example, a person with claustrophobic anxiety would be encouraged to visualize being in a small or tight place for a prolonged period of time.
- **Exposure to virtual reality:** When confronting the source of a phobia head-on is impractical, virtual reality technology might be employed as an alternative. Someone who is afraid of flying, for example, could use a flight simulator.
- **Exposed interoceptive:** This kind of exposure causes a specific bodily reaction to demonstrate that it is safe, despite being feared. For instance, someone who is afraid of feeling dizzy because they believe it leads to having a stroke could be prompted to spin around or get up quickly.

What Exactly Happens During Exposure Therapy?

During exposure therapy, therapists' methods change depending on the condition being treated. After determining what makes you anxious or fearful, your therapist or psychologist will begin treatment by gradually exposing you to the stimuli.

They frequently employ a graduated approach, exposing you to a minimally feared stimulus or a milder form of your trigger—all this in a secure and supervised setting. Your progress will determine how many sessions and how long it will take to complete your therapy.

If you're scared of spiders, for instance, the therapist could begin your first session by showing you photographs of them. They could bring a spider in a jar to the next session, and have you hold the spider during your third session.

Can I Use Exposure Treatment on Myself?

Typically, a therapist or medical professional will oversee an individual's exposure treatment sessions. In fact, a review of research published in 2018 showed that, in the treatment of OCD symptoms, therapist-directed exposure therapy showed superior results over self-directed treatment (Yetman, 2021). Moreover, attempting exposure therapy without assistance from a qualified expert can actually worsen trauma or terror. A severe disorder like PTSD shouldn't be self-treated.

To overcome moderate phobias, however, you may see improvement using some components of exposure therapy in your daily life.

Humans have an innate propensity to steer clear of things and circumstances that make them uncomfortable. Still, you could work up the courage to leave your comfort zone by forcing yourself to encounter your phobias. A person with mild social anxiety who feels uncomfortable in large groups, for instance, might willingly subject themselves to increasingly crowded environments to overcome their anxiety.

Exposure Therapy: How To Do It at Home

Professional psychologists are most suited to administer exposure therapy because they can help calm you down if your anxiety levels become too high and make sure you stick with the treatment even if you want to give up. Accountability is crucial, because if the anxiety becomes too intense and you stop your exposure before you have calmed down, you could increase your risk of experiencing anxiety in the future, making exposure treatment even more challenging.

In some cases, however, you could attempt to expose yourself to your fears at home or on your own. If you do, please consider the following:

- **Find out as much as possible about your anxiety.** Understanding the causes of your condition is crucial if you want to ensure your treatment is effective.
- **Create a plan of action detailing little steps you can take to alleviate your worry about a specific problem.** It may be challenging to build up to this naturally if you suffer from an obsession or panic disorder. That's why it is preferable to start slowly and work your way up. The cumulative exposures in the phobia instance included thinking about, examining photos of, standing in the same room as, and even touching the stimuli. Consider movies and other tools as well.
- **Have somebody to hold you responsible.** Remember that if you get too anxious and quit before you're completely calm, you risk worsening your anxiety. It is a good idea to have a support person who will hold you accountable and ensure that you do not opt out prematurely.
- **Study relaxation techniques.** Continue exposing yourself to the stimuli when you feel anxious until it stops having its negative affect. Since there are no pauses during treatment, you must ensure that you are equipped with relaxation techniques to prevent your worry from becoming too overwhelming.
- **Take it one step at a time.** Remember that a stimulus won't end unless you're no longer anxious while it's there. Do not move on to the next image if you are experiencing anxiety when viewing a picture of a spider. Wait until you are entirely free of your worry. To ensure your progress and be absolutely confident that this particular image is no longer triggering unease, you might do a follow-up test and expose yourself to those images again at a different time or setting. You should only go on to the next phase after you've passed the previous one.
- **You don't have to finish it all in one go.** You can quit and attempt it again the following day once you've determined that a specific stimulus aspect no longer makes you uneasy. Give yourself a well-deserved break.
- **Continue until you have effectively overcome the triggers that cause your anxiety.** You may need to practice daily or weekly with regular exposure to your fears, and eventually, they will start to dissipate.

- **After you're done, you must continue to test your abilities regularly.** Although overcoming anxiety is one thing, keeping it at bay is another. Don't consider yourself "done" only because you overcame one thing. To ensure that the anxiety never returns, keep up the exposure treatment even after it stops making you anxious.

A Final Word

If you believe it would benefit you, consult your doctor about locating a therapist who is skilled in the method. PTSD, OCD, and panic disorder are just a few of the phobias and anxiety disorders that might benefit from exposure therapy. Try-at-home versions of exposure therapy may also be suitable for those with milder anxiety issues.

Chapter 9:

Learning to Let Go

Carl Jung, the father of analytical psychology, wrote the phrase, "What you resist persists" (Maidenberg, 2022). And Jung sure knew what he was talking about!

When suffering is associated with an event or condition, the thought of accepting the way things are may be unsettling. Acceptance does not equate to resignation, the disappearance of the situation, or a general feeling of relief. Whether or not we accept something, the effect and feelings it produces are still there. It's when we add more layers of suffering to what already exists that intensifies the situation and makes it worse.

The concept of radical acceptance originated with psychologist Marsha Linehan's 1993 dialectical behavior therapy (DBT) proposal (Cunic, 2022). Originally, this kind of therapy was intended for intensely emotional borderline personality disorder patients, but it also helps with other problems, like eating disorders and depression.

Distress tolerance is a skill that DBT patients learn, and this enables them to avoid converting painful circumstances into longer-term suffering.

To practice radical acceptance, you must be willing to let go of the need to exert control over your environment and instead focus on merely seeing and accepting the present moment (Maidenberg, 2022).

Radical acceptance may be broken down into three parts:

- accepting that things are as they are
- realizing that unpleasant occurrences or circumstances have a root reason
- acknowledging that life is still worthwhile despite the pain

After practicing this for even a short while, you'll begin to feel greater calm, connection, and engagement in your interactions and community. As you let go of control and radically accept each of your emotions, you can learn to befriend yourself—and even forgive yourself. Your compassion and mindfulness grows.

The basic tenet is that non-acceptance, or resisting an emotion that arises, frequently results in misery. It's common to try to avoid, resist, or numb ourselves from uncomfortable realities via unhealthy coping techniques, such as engaging in unhealthy behaviors and relationships. Overeating, drinking and other unhealthy coping techniques might lead to a momentary feeling of "relief," however they mask the fundamental problem and will probably make you feel worse over time. Radical acceptance is the capacity to accept circumstances beyond your control without passing judgment and, in turn, reducing the pain these events might bring.

It contends that the secret to healing suffering is non-attachment, not holding on to a traumatic past. A lack of connection does not imply a lack of emotion, however. Instead, it's a determined decision to not let your suffering cause you more pain. Keeping a close eye on your internal state will help you realize when you're letting yourself feel down for no good reason. You don't have to get wrapped up in your current circumstance. Instead, accept your reality and resist the need to respond to it emotionally.

Signs of Radical Acceptance

Practicing radical acceptance in your life will take a conscious effort on your part that will not always come easily or naturally, especially when you are faced with extremely difficult circumstances.

When a traumatic event happens that you can't undo or change, or when something feels unjust, like losing a loved one or your career, I encourage you to practice radical acceptance. Even though sadness and disappointment are common feelings, real suffering happens when the pain persists because it is not accepted.

To practice radical acceptance does not, in any way, mean endorsing the current situation or your past experiences. Instead, since you are accepting reality and not trying to change it, it represents an opportunity for optimism.

This is easier said than done when things aren't going well, but allowing your emotions to run wild will only prolong your anguish and misery. Avoiding or dwelling on a situation might indeed make you feel worse!

Radical acceptance entails offering yourself compassion.

Signs of Rejection

When you start paying attention to the patterns in your thinking, feelings, and relationships, you may become aware of occurrences or circumstances that you have not accepted in the past. Here are some examples.

Patterns in thought processes:

- *This is more than I can handle.*
- *That is unfair.*
- *This is not how things should be.*
- *I refuse to accept that this is occurring.*
- *This is wrong.*
- *Things need to be different.*
- *When will this stop?*

Emotional patterns and actions:

- Every negative event in your life is something you blame on yourself.
- You feel trapped and discouraged about making positive changes.
- You want things to be different, yet you feel helpless to change them.
- You're upset with everything in life.
- You use inappropriate coping skills, such as alcohol or drugs.

Patterns of relationships:

- To get your partner to change, you badger them continuously.
- You frequently feel let down by the decisions made by others.
- You harbor resentment toward events of the past.
- You often hold grudges.

Can you recognize yourself in any of these patterns? If so, now is the time to accept that this is how you have been and make a pledge to yourself to develop healthier thoughts and habits so that you may start to live a lighter, more positive life.

Where Radical Acceptance Originates

Although suffering will always exist, radical acceptance entails shifting your focus from emotional outbursts and helplessness to cool, collected reasoning. You might not be able to alter the actual circumstances of a situation. Still, you have complete control over how you see it and react.

Distress tolerance conveys acceptance and emotional distance rather than the approval of a circumstance. It allows you to focus on the things you can manage and frees up your mental and spiritual resources so you can take better care of yourself.

Breathe in deeply, and as you exhale, let go of resentment and relinquish negative feelings. It is feasible to develop ideas and create strategies for change if these feelings have been dispelled.

In DBT, the term "wise mind" combines the rational and emotional aspects of your thinking to achieve harmony. A wise mind is able to act deliberately after letting go of the emotionally-charged component of this radical acceptance problem-solving approach. In this context, the term "acceptance" does not mean agreeing with or condoning a particular situation, but instead accepting it "as is" so that you may move on with your life.

How To Apply Radical Acceptance

Discover more about what you can do to strengthen your capacity to practice radical acceptance. Keep in mind that, like all the other techniques highlighted in this book, this is a skill that improves with time and practice.

- Pay attention to the things that cause resistance and become aware of your inability to accept something.
- Remind yourself that reality cannot be changed at this time. As the saying goes, "It is what it is."
- It's necessary to remind yourself that you can't have control over everything that happens to you and that there are always outside factors that contribute to any situation.
- Consider how things would be if you agreed to the circumstances.
- To comprehend your emotions, try relaxation techniques, mindfulness exercises, journaling, and self-reflection.

- Allow yourself to experience your feelings fully and safely. Feelings need to be felt, not ignored.
- Consider the physical resonance of your feelings. Is there any discomfort or a restriction in your body? Pay attention to what this is trying to tell you.
- Recognize that life may still be valuable even when you're hurting.
- Practice mindful meditation and radical acceptance to improve your journey.

The following suggestions can help you stop dwelling on "what could have been" so you can start enjoying the "here and now" more fully (Parincu, n.d.).

- **Acknowledge the present**. The most vital step is to be aware of your circumstances and accept them without passing strong judgment. This does not imply that you should put up with abusive or deceptive behavior, but that you must accept the facts as they are, regardless of how you may feel about them. For instance, you could discover that your house is without electricity when you wake up one morning. Either you allow yourself to become enraged and remark that something like this should not have occurred on such a significant day, or you choose not to and light a candle instead. You accept that it is a challenging situation, actively think about your next steps, and devise a solution instead.
- **Do you have any power to influence or alter the situation?** Why are you becoming furious if you have no control over what's happening? It's hard to accept that you can't always fix things, but that realization actually leads to a sense of freedom. When it rains, we have no choice but to accept it.
- **Set aside your bias.** Radical acceptance means putting judgment aside and accepting things as they are. You may hone your mindfulness abilities by meditating regularly and paying attention to the present.
- **The past has passed.** Keep in mind that nothing can be done to change the past. It's not easy going through difficult times, and whether it was good or horrible, the past happened.
- **Breathe.** Although it seems straightforward, we often forget to breathe properly. Whenever you resist reality, your body might tense up in certain areas, like your shoulders, face, or stomach.

Breathing can be extremely powerful, so take a moment to consciously inhale and exhale deeply. Pay attention to how your body changes and how this makes you feel. You can learn to center yourself in the present moment and unwind by practicing breath awareness.

- **Be deliberate.** Make the decision to engage in daily radical acceptance practice and recognize that it requires effort to become proficient. It's silly to assume that you'll instantly let go of all negativity when you practice this skill for the first time. Make sure to apply this technique regularly, and you'll quickly see how it enhances your life.

There is a wealth of information on radical acceptance, including books, podcasts, and websites. Seeking professional support from a therapist might be helpful if you are having trouble processing your emotions on your own.

Statements to Help With Radical Acceptance

You can use the coping statements below if you feel unable to accept reality and go on. Keep these close by so you can remember them next time you suddenly feel out of control.

- *Fighting back against bad feelings simply magnifies them.*
- *The events of the past are beyond my power to alter them.*
- *I can accept things as they are in the current moment.*
- *Even if it's challenging, I can overcome challenging feelings.*
- *I'm going to get through this, whatever happens.*
- *Despite how awful this feels right now, I know I can get through this and that this emotion will eventually pass.*
- *Even if I'm experiencing nervousness, I can still effectively handle this situation.*
- *If I can come to terms with what has happened, I can still find happiness.*
- *Even though I feel horrible, I can choose a different course.*
- *I'm better equipped to make wise decisions and find solutions to issues when I maintain my senses.*
- *Taking the appropriate steps is preferable to continuing to judge or point the finger.*

Insight Meditation and Radical Acceptance

Everyone can practice mindfulness and meditation, which, as you know, have several benefits on our mental health. We know that a regular meditation routine can help us feel calmer, less stressed, and even happier (Parincu, n.d.). But did you know that radical acceptance and mindfulness are interconnected processes that support each other's growth patterns?

Spending some time in meditation can help you develop radical acceptance—and the other way around. Your capacity to accept life can only improve as you practice bringing gentle attention to your discomforts.

Radical acceptance guided meditations are valuable and widely available. I suggest you try Tara Brach's meditation by following the link below. Tara Brach is a forerunner in radical acceptance and mindfulness! https://youtu.be/hUQiGJBcv6Q

When to Practice Radical Acceptance

Of course, there are certain circumstances when practicing radical acceptance is simply not the right move. The majority of these concern circumstances when trying to change the situation is wiser than accepting things as they are. Be ready to take more determined, drastic action if, for example:

- someone is mistreating or abusing you, or if you're in an abusive relationship
- if you are feeling unappreciated, disrespected, or exploited at work, if you are feeling burned out from your present circumstances, or if you just don't feel like giving it another try
- when you purposefully don't do anything because you're afraid

On the other hand, the following circumstances would greatly benefit from applying radical acceptance. Although these scenarios may appear to be just as challenging as those mentioned above, they are unchangeable and something you may not have any control over:

- if you are experiencing a relationship breakup
- if you see an unanticipated shift, such as a job loss
- when a loved one passes away
- if you've been through a horrible encounter, such as neglect or abuse as a child

- if you are denying what happened and suppressing your feelings
- if you feel trapped or are having trouble getting over a bad experience
- if you have attempted alternative methods of dealing with your pain but they have failed

Various Forms of Acceptance

Now, let's look at the comparisons between radical acceptance and mindfulness techniques, as well as the differences between radical acceptance and ordinary acceptance.

- **Mindfulness:** Being mindful reminds us to focus on the present moment, which is also the only technique for practicing radical acceptance. As you may know, mindfulness has its roots in the Buddhist practice of preserving a tranquil, zen-like state. When you are attentive, you are present in the situation without thinking about it or passing judgment. The ultimate objective of mindfulness is to develop radical acceptance.
- **Ordinary acceptance:** While "acceptance" in its common sense frequently involves an agreement with a given circumstance, "radical acceptance" does not require such agreement. Instead, radical acceptance aims to lead you to a place where you can perceive the choices in your situation.

For instance, if you suffer from chronic pain, you can hold on to the conviction that life is worthwhile even though it sometimes causes agony. Radical acceptance is the notion of living your life in this way.

By following the principles of radical acceptance, you might feel relieved and have a more positive outlook on your circumstances. You are balancing the need to change with the need to accept your fortune in life.

Ironically, sometimes you have to accept what's happened before you can go forward and make the adjustments that would make you feel better about your circumstances.

The Last Word

Although it may be difficult initially, radical acceptance can help you feel better as you learn to deal with painful experiences.

When you realize you're in one of those circumstances, you must be ready to accept your feelings and move on. Even if it isn't simple right away, you should notice that things in your life start improving with time. When things begin to turn around for you, life generally begins to seem lighter and less taxing, allowing you to make any additional changes more easily. Daily acceptance training strengthens self-compassion and prepares you for life's most trying challenges.

Radical acceptance emphasizes embracing reality as it is and re-alizing it is worthwhile to live even when faced with challenging circumstances.

Conclusion:

A Life of Serenity

And there you are, in the not-so-distant future. You find yourself in front of the mirror and think *I feel lighter today*. You have a better understanding of who you are and the journey you have fought through to get to this very day. You feel in control of yourself and brave enough to face whatever life may confront you with. At this moment, you are in complete acceptance of who you are and feel a deep empathy as you contemplate what you have overcome thus far. You. A perfectly imperfect woman. A woman who hasn't given up. A woman who has put in the work to understand herself better and seek help. You know that today and every day hereafter may not be without trial, but right now, at least for this moment, you can say with confidence that you will be okay.

Imagine how empowered you would feel if you took just one small step into doing something different today.

If you choose to change nothing, then nothing will change. Take even only one small thing from this book and start to practice it every day—that alone is more productive and will yield better results than not doing anything. Consistency is key.

On a similar note, attempting to apply everything you've learned all at once and taking off running with it may be counterproductive. If you did that, you might quickly find yourself falling off the bandwagon, getting discouraged, or considering quitting.

Select the healing techniques that feel best for you and put your whole heart into them. This is your time and your space to work towards the best possible version of yourself.

Living without anxiety means being freed from the need to seek out others' approval. It is accepting who you are and what you stand for as you make your way to peace. It's about giving up artificial labels that have never served you well in the first place.

The key to living without worry is to feel at ease with yourself and have genuine self-confidence consistently.

You will see results depending on how often you use the techniques in this book and if you use them correctly. You may see signs of improvement when you have more energy to concentrate on your daily tasks, when the anxiety episodes become less frequent, and when your self-talk switches from self-criticism to self-compassion.

It only takes a few minutes every day to practice these mindfulness exercises. There's no need to meditate on it for hours—although doing so might be helpful. Use this guide on its own or in conjunction with the advice provided by your healthcare provider. With this easy-to-follow, step-by-step advice, I hope that you have learned how to recognize and evaluate your anxiety symptoms and develop the strength to overcome your fears. You are unstoppable!

You are worthy.

You are capable.

You are calm.

Although this may sound like an overdone cliché, you should know that you are not the only one embarking on a journey to heal from anxiety. Despite what you may think, you are not alone in your challenges. I want you to experience the acceptance you need to overcome obstacles and live a happy, fulfilling life. Have a positive attitude and a grateful heart. Coming to grips with your diagnosis is the first step toward a better, happier future. Healing is a lifetime process.

Your healing journey will most likely be a slow and steady adventure. It will be challenging at times, but you will benefit from your consistent efforts in the long run. Have patience and compassion with yourself on your harder days. As you work to implement tools and venture onto a new path, give yourself credit for the victories along the way, no matter how small. Above all else, keep going! Be prepared to show up for yourself. You are worthy and capable of being free of suffering. Give yourself permission to heal.

About the Author

Maiya Wolf is a mother of two who currently resides in the Pacific Northwest, USA. A former super anxious woman, she now specializes in helping others reclaim their freedom in their mental health journey by using a mindful and intentional approach. She is a passionate author who believes every woman deserves to feel empowered by their own strength—no matter what battle they may face. *Healing the Anxious Woman* is the first of many to come in the *Lighter Healing* series.

For more information on new releases and other exclusive Maiya content, Please check out her website here: subscribepage.io/l46nhW

References

• Abraham, M. (2020, October 20). How to Perform Exposure Therapy for Anxiety at Home. Calm Clinic. https://www.calmclinic.com/anxiety/treatment/exposure-therapy

• Anxiety disorders - symptoms and causes. (2018, May 4). Mayo Clinic; Mayo Foundation for Medical Education and Research. https://www.mayoclinic.org/diseases-conditions/anxiety/symptoms-causes/syc-20350961

• Carpenter, D. (2018). The Science Behind Gratitude (and How It Can Change Your Life). Happify. https://www.happify.com/hd/the-science-behind-gratitude/

• Cherry, K. (2019). What Is Behind the Psychology of Positive Thinking? Verywell Mind. https://www.verywellmind.com/what-is-positive-thinking-2794772

• Chowdhury, M. R. (2019, April 9). The Neuroscience of Gratitude and How It Affects Anxiety & Grief. Positive Psychology. https://positivepsychology.com/neuroscience-of-gratitude/

• Cuncic, A. (2021, May 26). What Is Radical Acceptance? Verywell Mind. https://www.verywellmind.com/what-is-radical-acceptance-5120614

• Dr. Kathleen Allen. (2019, November 23). Giving Thanks to Nature. Kathleen Allen. https://kathleenallen.net/giving-thanks-to-nature/

• Guarnotta, E. (2022, February 2). Anxiety in Women: Symptoms, Causes, & Treatments. Choosing Therapy. https://www.choosingtherapy.com/anxiety-in-women/

• How to Heal Your Metabolism with Kate Deering. (2021). On YouTube. https://www.youtube.com/watch?v=caUOJWnMK4g

• How to Meditate with Anxiety. (2021, June 30). Mindful. https://www.mindful.org/mindfulness-meditation-anxiety/#:~:text=How%20Mindfulness%20Calms%20Anxious%20Feelings

• Maidenberg, M. P. (2022, March 3). The Healing Power of Radical Acceptance. Psychology Today. https://www.psychologytoday.com/za/blog/being-your-best-self/202203/the-healing-power-radical-acceptance

• Mairanz, A. (2018, April 23). Overcoming Barriers to Setting Boundaries. Empower Your Mind Therapy. https://eymtherapy.com/blog/barriers-to-setting-boundaries/

• Martin, S. (2019, May 31). What Is Self-Love and Why Is It So Important? Psych Central. https://psychcentral.com/blog/imperfect/2019/05/what-is-self-love-and-why-is-it-so-important

• National Institute of Mental Health. (2017). Any Anxiety Disorder. Www.nimh.nih. gov. https://www.nimh.nih.gov/health/statistics/any-anxiety-disorder

• Paul, Dr. M. (2017, September 8). Choose Yourself: Why Self-Love Heals Anxiety. Thought Catalog. https://thoughtcatalog.com/dr-margaret-paul/2017/09/choose-your-self-why-self-love-heals-anxiety/

- Snee, M. (2020, December 28). Consistency is key: Physically and Mentally. Mt-2club. https://mt2club.com/blog/2020/12/28/consistency-is-key

- Star, K. (2019a). A Step-by-Step Guide to Using Progressive Muscle Relaxation (PMR). Verywell Mind. https://www.verywellmind.com/progressive-muscle-relaxation-pmr-2584097

- Team, M. (2017, December 11). What Does Self Awareness Mean? How Do You Practice Self Awareness? Mindworks Meditation. https://mindworks.org/blog/what-does-self-awareness-mean/

- The Johari Window Model. (2014, July 10). Communication Theory. https://www.communicationtheory.org/the-johari-window-model/

- Uma Naidoo, MD. (2016, April 13). Nutritional strategies to ease anxiety. Harvard Health Blog. https://www.health.harvard.edu/blog/nutritional-strategies-to-ease-anxiety-201604139441

- Vago, D. R., & Silbersweig, D. A. (2012). Self-awareness, self-regulation, and self-transcendence (S-ART): a framework for understanding the neurobiological mechanisms of mindfulness. Frontiers in Human Neuroscience, 6. Frontiersin. https://doi.org/10.3389/fnhum.2012.00296

- Van Minnen, A., Harned, M. S., Zoellner, L., & Mills, K. (2012). Examining potential contraindications for prolonged exposure therapy for PTSD. European Journal of Psychotraumatology, 3(1), 18805. https://doi.org/10.3402/ejpt.v3i0.18805

- Villines, Z. (2022, June 20). Cognitive restructuring: Steps, technique, and examples. Medical News Today. https://www.medicalnewstoday.com/articles/cognitive-restructuring

- What Is Exposure Therapy? (2017). American Psychological Association. https://www.apa.org/ptsd-guideline/patients-and-families/exposure-therapy

- Abraham, M. (2020, October 20). How to Perform Exposure Therapy for Anxiety at Home. Calm Clinic. https://www.calmclinic.com/anxiety/treatment/exposure-therapy

- Alvord, M., & Halfond, R. (2021). What's the difference between stress and anxiety? American Psychological Association. https://www.apa.org/topics/stress/anxiety-difference#:~:text=People%20under%20stress%20experience%20mental

- Borenstein, J. (2020, February 12). Self-Love and What It Means. Brain & Behavior Research Foundation. https://www.bbrfoundation.org/blog/self-love-and-what-it-means

- Brussat, F., & Brussat, M. A. (2022). Gratitude as a Spiritual Practice. Spirituality and Practice. https://www.spiritualityandpractice.com/practices/alphabet/view/13/gratitude

- Carpenter, D. (2018). The Science Behind Gratitude (and How It Can Change Your Life). Happify. https://www.happify.com/hd/the-science-behind-gratitude/

- Cherry, K. (2019). What Is Behind the Psychology of Positive Thinking? Verywell Mind. https://www.verywellmind.com/what-is-positive-thinking-2794772

- Chowdhury, M. R. (2019, April 9). The Neuroscience of Gratitude and How It Affects Anxiety & Grief. Positive Psychology. https://positivepsychology.com/neuroscience-of-gratitude/

- Dr. Kathleen Allen. (2019, November 23). Giving Thanks to Nature. Kathleen Allen. https://kathleenallen.net/giving-thanks-to-nature/

- Eagleson, C., Hayes, S., Mathews, A., Perman, G., & Hirsch, C. R. (2016). The power of positive thinking: Pathological worry is reduced by thought replacement in Generalized Anxiety Disorder. Behaviour Research and Therapy, 78, 13–18. https://doi.org/10.1016/j.brat.2015.12.017

- Foods to Avoid If You Have Anxiety or Depression. (2017). WebMD. https://www.webmd.com/depression/ss/slideshow-avoid-foods-anxiety-depression

- Gillihan, S. J., Williams, M. T., Malcoun, E., Yadin, E., & Foa, E. B. (2012). Common pitfalls in exposure and response prevention (EX/RP) for OCD. Journal of Obsessive-Compulsive and Related Disorders, 1(4), 251–257. https://doi.org/10.1016/j.jocrd.2012.05.002

- Harvard Health Publishing. (2021, August 14). Giving thanks can make you happier. Harvard Health. https://www.health.harvard.edu/healthbeat/giving-thanks-can-make-you-happier

- Hofmann, S. G., Sawyer, A. T., Witt, A. A., & Oh, D. (2010). The effect of mindfulness-based therapy on anxiety and depression: A meta-analytic review. Journal of Consulting and Clinical Psychology, 78(2), 169–183. https://doi.org/10.1037/a0018555

- How to Heal Your Metabolism with Kate Deering. (2021). On YouTube. https://www.youtube.com/watch?v=caUOJWnMK4g

- How to Meditate with Anxiety. (2021, June 30). Mindful. https://www.mindful.org/mindfulness-meditation-anxiety/#:~:text=How%20Mindfulness%20Calms%20Anxious%20Feelings

- Journaling for Mental Health. (2019). University of Rochester Medical Center. https://www.urmc.rochester.edu/encyclopedia/content.aspx?ContentID=4552&ContentTypeID=1

- Kaplan, J. S., & Tolin, D. F. (2011, September 7). Exposure Therapy for Anxiety Disorders. Psychiatric Times. https://www.psychiatrictimes.com/view/exposure-therapy-anxiety-disorders

- Maidenberg, M. P. (2022, March 3). The Healing Power of Radical Acceptance. Psychology Today. https://www.psychologytoday.com/za/blog/being-your-best-self/202203/the-healing-power-radical-acceptance

- Manson, M. (2013, January 14). The Guide to Strong Relationships. Mark Manson. https://markmanson.net/boundaries

• National Institute of Mental Health. (2017). Any Anxiety Disorder. Www.nimh.nih. gov. https://www.nimh.nih.gov/health/statistics/any-anxiety-disorder

• Paul, Dr. M. (2017, September 8). Choose Yourself: Why Self-Love Heals Anxiety. Thought Catalog. https://thoughtcatalog.com/dr-margaret-paul/2017/09/choose-your-self-why-self-love-heals-anxiety/

• Razzetti, G. (2019, April 29). The Johari Window Exercise - Increase self-awareness and team awareness. Fearless Culture. https://www.fearlessculture.design/blog-posts/the-johari-window

• Snee, M. (2020, December 28). Consistency is key: Physically and Mentally. Mt-2club. https://mt2club.com/blog/2020/12/28/consistency-is-key

• Sutton, J. (2022, January 28). How to Use Mindfulness Therapy for Anxiety: 15 Exercises. Positive Psychology. https://positivepsychology.com/mindfulness-for-anxiety/

• Vago, D. R., & Silbersweig, D. A. (2012). Self-awareness, self-regulation, and self-transcendence (S-ART): a framework for understanding the neurobiological mechanisms of mindfulness. Frontiers in Human Neuroscience, 6. Frontiersin. https://doi.org/10.3389/fnhum.2012.00296

• What Is Exposure Therapy? (2017). American Psychological Association. https://www.apa.org/ptsd-guideline/patients-and-families/exposure-therapy

• Young, K. (2016, December 16). 13 Different Ways to Practice Mindfulness - And the Difference it Can Make. Hey Sigmund. https://www.heysigmund.com/different-ways-to-practice-mindfulness/

• Zahn, C. (2021, July 7). Anxiety: How Women Can Cope. Kettering Health. https://ketteringhealth.org/anxiety-and-how-women-can-cope/

• Zoffness, R. (2019, December 20). How to Set Boundaries With Family | Psychology Today. Psychology Today. https://www.psychologytoday.com/us/blog/pain-ex-plained/201912/how-set-boundaries-familyttps://www.heysigmund.com/different-ways-to-practice-mindfulness/

• Zahn, C. (2021, July 7). Anxiety: How Women Can Cope. Kettering Health. https://ketteringhealth.org/anxiety-and-how-women-can-cope/